ADULT READING SERIES
Challenger 2

COREA
MURPHY

NEW READERS PRESS

Syracuse, New York

0-88336-782-3

Copyright © 1985 New Readers Press
New Readers Press
Division of ProLiteracy Worldwide
1320 Jamesville Avenue, Syracuse, New York 13210
www.newreaderspress.com

Printed in the United States of America
20   19   18

All proceeds from the sale of New Readers Press materials
support literacy programs in the United States and worldwide.

Designer: Chris Steenwerth
Cover Designer: Chris Steenwerth
Cover Photo: Jeffrey L. Rotman

About the Author

Corea Murphy has worked in the field of education since the early 1960s. In addition to classroom and tutorial teaching, Ms. Murphy has developed language arts curriculum guides for public high schools, conducted curriculum and effectiveness workshops, and established an educational program for residents in a drug rehabilitation facility.

Ms. Murphy became interested in creating a reading series for older students when she began working with adults and adolescents in the early 1970s. The **Challenger Adult Reading Series** is the result of her work with these students.

In a very real sense, the students contributed greatly to the development of this reading series. Their enthusiasm for learning to read and their willingness to work hard provided inspiration, and their many helpful suggestions influenced the content of both the student books and the teacher's manuals.

It is to these students that the **Challenger Adult Reading Series** is dedicated with the hope that others who wish to become good readers will find this reading program both helpful and stimulating.

A special note of gratitude is also extended to Kay Koschnick, Christina Jagger, and Mary Hutchison of New Readers Press for their work and support in guiding this series to completion.

Table of Contents

Lesson 1

Sneezing

Words for Study

cover	January	Pinocchio	sense
dust	has	children	mouth
recorded	ugly	every	touch
Clark	doctor	somebody	draw

Sneezing

At one time or another, everybody sneezes. If somebody is around to hear the sneezing, he often says, "God bless you." Most people cover their noses when they sneeze, so their germs won't go all over the room. Some things that often make people sneeze are dust, cat hairs, weeds, black pepper, and colds.

The worst sneezing fit ever recorded was that of a seventeen-year-old girl named June Clark. She started sneezing on January 4, 1966, and didn't stop until June 8, 1966.

1 **About the Reading.** Answer these questions.

1. Why do most people cover their noses when they sneeze?

_____

2. What do people often say when they hear somebody sneeze?

_____

3. List three things that often make people sneeze.

_____   _____   _____

4. How old was June Clark when she had her sneezing fit? _____

5. For how many months did June Clark sneeze? _____

What do you think?

6. Do you find that you sneeze more in the spring or the fall?

_____

2 Word Sounds.

Pick the right answer and fill it in on the line. Then write all three words at the left. Check your answer to make sure it makes sense. Note how the first one has been done.

1. (*c, gr,* or *sh*) Do you like the ___sh___ape of your nose?

_____cape_____

_____grape_____

_____shape_____

2. (*dr, st,* or *th*) Many people _____ink that their noses are ugly.

_____

_____

_____

3. (*ch, r,* or *str*) If they have the money, they can get a doctor to _____ange the shape of their noses.

_____

_____

_____

4. (*ch, gr,* or *kn*) Pinocchio is a little boy in a children's story. Every time he told a lie, his nose _____ew very long.

_____

_____

_____

5. (*cr, dr,* or *tr*) Somebody who always _____ies to know what other people are doing is called nosy.

_____

_____

_____

6. (*bl, j,* or *sn*) Somebody who walks around with his nose in the air is often called a _____ob.

_____

_____

7. (*bl*, *gr*, or *kn*) Do you know the name of the deer in the Christmas song

_____ who is _____own for his red nose?

_____

_____

8. (*Sm*, *Sp*, or *Sw*) _____elling is one of the five senses.

_____

_____

_____

9. (*br*, *ch*, or *sm*) People who _____oke cigarettes can't smell as well as people
who don't.

_____

_____

_____

10. (*bl*, *p*, or *st*) People who have _____uffed up noses from bad colds can't
smell well at all.

_____

_____

_____

3 **Matching.** Match the part of the body with the right sense.

hearing _____ 1. ear
seeing
smelling _____ 2. eye
tasting _____ 3. hand
touching
_____ 4. mouth

_____ 5. nose

4 **Marking the _e_'s.** Mark the _e_'s in these words. If the sound for _e_ is long, draw a line over it. If the sound for _e_ is short, draw a curved line over it. If you don't hear the _e_ at all, draw a line through it.

1. thēsé   5. harmless   9. remind

2. ĕnd   6. next   10. sweat

3. alone   7. useful   11. close

4. bleed   8. pancake   12. choose

5 **Words That Sound the Same.** These words sound the same, but they do not have the same meaning. Put the right word on each line.

eye _and_ I   1. _____ can't see as well when my right _____ is covered.

hear _and_ here   2. Mrs. Clark did not _____ her child say, "Did you know that the doctor is _____?"

two _and_ to   3. _____ people won free passes _____ the movies.

dear _and_ deer   4. When the little boy heard the gun go off, he prayed, "_____ God, I hope the _____ wasn't hurt."

for _and_ four   5. When the flames burst from the first floor of the house, _____ children ran _____ help.

knows _and_ nose   6. Pinocchio _____ that his _____ will get bigger every time he tells a lie.

Lesson 2

Cats

Lee Snider/Photo Images

Words for Study

animals	country	catty	catbird
own	sometimes	catcall	chestnuts
dim	leave	noise	its
United States	describe	speaker	purr

Cats

Many people like having cats for house pets. Cats are one of the smartest animals. They can see better in dim light than man or any other animal. Their eyes shine in the dark. Cats also have sharp senses of smell and hearing. However, because cats like to have their own way, it takes longer to train a cat as a pet than it takes to train a dog.

The United States has more cats than any other country. It has been recorded that more than twenty-eight million cats live in the United States.

People who love cats can do strange things sometimes. A doctor on the West Coast, who died in 1963, left $415,000 to his two fifteen-year-old cats in his will.

1 About the Reading. Answer these questions.

1. Which country has the most cats? _____

2. How many cats does this country have? _____

3. How much money did the man on the West Coast leave his two cats? _____

4. What had been this man's job? _____

5. What can a cat do better than man or any other animal?

_____

What do you think?

6. Which do you think make better pets–cats or dogs–and why?

_____

_____

2 Word Sounds. Pick the right answer and fill it in on the line. Then write all three words at the left. Check your answer to make sure it makes sense.

1. (*br, gr,* or *st*)   Some people can't _____and to be around cats because
   they make them sneeze.

   _____

   _____

   _____

2. (*cr, j,* or *sl*)   Others can't stand to be around cats because these animals

   _____   give them the _____eeps.

   _____

   _____

3. (*f, s,* or *sl*)   The word *cat* is also a _____ang word that people sometimes use
   to describe a man.

   _____

   _____

   _____

4. (*b, cl,* or *m*)   Women are called *catty* if they are _____ean or full of spite toward others.

_____

_____

_____

5. (*cl, h,* or *n*)   You don't often _____ear men called *catty* or women called *cats*.

_____

_____

_____

6. (*shr, sk,* or *sp*)   A catcall is a _____ill noise that people make when they don't like what a speaker is saying.

_____

_____

_____

7. (*br, cl,* or *cr*)   A catbird has a black _____own and tail and makes a sound like that of a cat.

_____

_____

_____

8. (*p, r,* or *str*)   There is a story about a monkey that uses a cat's _____aw to rake chestnuts out of a fire.

_____

_____

_____

9. (*c, h,* or *n*)   _____ow the word *cat's-paw* is used to describe people who are used by others to do something that is full of danger.

_____

_____

10. (*s*, *sp*, or *t*)   The largest fish which _____ends its whole life in fresh water
is a catfish.

_____

_____

_____

3   **Putting Words in Classes.** Put the words that have to do with cats in
List A. Put the words that have to do with dogs in **List B**.

always land on their feet   digging up bones
barking   man's best friend
chasing cars   nine lives
climbing trees   purring

List A: Cats   **List B: Dogs**

1. _____   1. _____

2. _____   2. _____

3. _____   3. _____

4. _____   4. _____

4   **Words That Sound the Same.** Put the right word on each line.

buy *and* by   1. _____ the time Linda got through shopping, she had no money left

to _____ food for dinner.

knew *and* new   2. Ben _____ a man who would tear up his work and start all over

on a _____ page even if he made only one mistake.

ate *and* eight   3. When Dave got home from work last night, he _____

_____ hot dogs for dinner.

do *and* due   4. "_____ you know what time the plane is _____?" asked Mary.

hour *and* our   5. "_____ plane should be here in an _____," said her aunt.

Lesson 3

The Number Seven

Words for Study

Rome	world	human	tailor	someone
deadly	break	renewed	killed	scroll
sin	mirror	smoker	Bible	seal
sea	period	spent	seventh	anger

The Number Seven

There are seven days in a week, the Seven Hills of Rome, seven deadly sins, and the seven seas of the world. Seven is a lucky number for many people. Seven is also said to be the number of years you have bad luck after you break a mirror.

There are other facts to know about a seven-year period of time. Seven years is how long it takes for every cell in the human body to be renewed. By law, a person is recorded as dead if he has been missing for seven years.

And it took one woman who had been a smoker seven years to save $1,500. This is how much money she would have spent on cigarettes if she hadn't decided to quit smoking.

1 **About the Reading.** Answer these questions.

1. How long did it take the woman who quit smoking to save $1,500? _____

2. Name the city that is on seven hills. _____

3. How is somebody recorded who has been missing for seven years? _____

4. What do some people think will happen if you break a mirror?

_____

5. What happens in the human body over a seven-year period of time?

_____

6. If you smoke, how much money would you save in *one* year if you quit? _____

2 **Word Sounds.** Pick the right answer and fill it in on the line. Then write all three words at the left. Check your answer to make sure it makes sense.

1. (*bl*, *dr*, or *th*)   Do you _____ink you will have seven years of bad luck if you break a mirror?

   _____

   _____

   _____

2. (*br*, *c*, or *w*)   Do you know the story of the _____ave little tailor who killed seven flies in one blow?

   _____

   _____

   _____

3. (*bl*, *g*, or *fr*)   *Seven-Up* is the name of a card _____ame.

   _____

   _____

   _____

4. (*bl*, *dr*, or *st*)   It is also the name of a soft _____ink.

   _____

   _____

   _____

5. (*d*, *pr*, or *sp*)   You need a lucky pair of _____ice to roll the number seven seven times in a row.

   _____

   _____

   _____

6. (*d*, *pl*, or *st*)   In the first book of the Bible, it is _____ated that on the seventh day, God rested from his work.

   _____

   _____

   _____

7. (*b*, *c*, or *thr*)   In the last book of the Bible, someone sitting on a _____one has a scroll with seven seals.

_____

_____

_____

8. (*ch*, *p*, or *st*)   A movie called *The Seventh Seal* is based on this _____art of the Bible.

_____

_____

_____

9. (*ch*, *p*, or *w*)   The seventh day of the _____eek is Saturday.

_____

_____

_____

10. (*ch*, *gr*, or *s*)   Two of the seven deadly _____ins are pride and anger.

_____

_____

_____

3   **Word Sounds.** If the *ow* in the word at the left sounds like the *ow* in *cow*, write the word in the first list. If the *ow* in the word sounds like the *ow* in *slow*, write the word in the last list.

blow	**Cow**	**Slow**
clown		
crowd	1. _____	1. _____
grown		
how	2. _____	2. _____
know	3. _____	3. _____
now		
show	4. _____	4. _____
snow	5. _____	5. _____
wow		

4 Number Words. Read these number words.

twenty (20)	thirty (30)	hundred (100)
twenty-one (21)	thirty-one (31)	thousand (1,000)
twenty-two (22)	forty (40)	million (1,000,000)
twenty-three (23)	fifty (50)	
twenty-four (24)	sixty (60)	
twenty-five (25)	seventy (70)	
twenty-six (26)	eighty (80)	
twenty-seven (27)	ninety (90)	
twenty-eight (28)		
twenty-nine (29)		

Answer these questions by writing the words for the numbers on the line.

_____ 1. How many hours are in a day?

_____ 2. How many days are in the month of January?

_____ 3. How many days are in the month of June?

_____ 4. How many states are in the United States?

_____ 5. How many hours a week do most people work at their jobs?

_____ 6. If a man was born in 1960, how old was he in 1985?

_____ 7. How old were you on your last birthday?

_____ 8. How old would you like to be when you celebrate your very last birthday?

Do you know?

_____ 9. By law, how old do you have to be to drive a car in this state?

_____ 10. By law, how old do you have to be to quit school in this state?

Lesson 4

A Few Facts about Beer

Kathryn Raymond

Words for Study

term	quarts	gallons	reacts
English	meant	*Mayflower*	strongly
pubs	size	sailed	sunlight
England	drank	further	cloudy
pints	Egypt	instead	second

A Few Facts about Beer

● Did your mother, father, or a teacher ever tell you to "mind your p's and q's"? This term comes from English pubs. (Bars in England are called pubs.) The *p* stands for pint. The *q* stands for quart. At first, minding your p's and q's meant counting the size and number of the mugs of beer that the people in the pub drank.

● People have been drinking beer for over 3,500 years. A long, long time ago, one ruler in Egypt gave away 30,000 gallons of beer each year as a gift to the gods.

● It is also recorded that the people who sailed to this country on the *Mayflower* would have gone further south instead of landing in New England if they had not run out of beer. Beer had been food for these people. When their beer ran out, the ship had to land so they could try to find more food.

● Beer reacts strongly to light. In sunlight, beer turns cloudy and takes on a funny smell and taste. People who love beer think that the best way to drink it is to pour the beer into a glass. They also say that beer should always have some kind of head when it is served.

Adapted with permission from Aug., 1977 *Reader's Digest*.
Copyright ©1977 by The Reader's Digest Association, Inc. "Here's to Good Old Beer" by John Ennis.

1 About the Reading. Answer these questions.

1. What do the people who live in England call a bar? _____

2. What do the *p* and *q* really stand for in the term "minding your p's and q's"?

   _____

3. What did one ruler in Egypt do every year?

   _____

4. Why did the *Mayflower* land in New England instead of sailing further south?

   _____

5. What happens to beer if it is left in the sunlight?

   _____

6. How do people who really like beer say it should be served?

   _____

Do you know?

7. What do you think the term, "minding your p's and q's," means when your mother, father, or a teacher says it?

   _____

8. In what year did the *Mayflower* land on the New England coast? _____

2 **Word Sounds.** Pick the right answer and fill it in on the line. Then write all three words at the left. Check your answer to make sure it makes sense.

1. (*br, ch,* or *st*)   The world's strongest beer was _____ewed in England in 1968.

_____

_____

_____

2. (*c, f,* or *h*)   Mr. Hill of England _____olds the world's record for drinking more beer in 6½ seconds than anybody else.

_____

_____

_____

3. (*ch, r,* or *str*)   There are many _____ange records about eating and drinking.

_____

_____

_____

4. (*b, j,* or *m*)   In 1973, a man ate 1,510 cold baked _____eans one by one in thirty minutes.

_____

_____

_____

5. (*a, da,* or *sta*)   In 1956, a man _____te forty-four hard-boiled eggs in thirty minutes.

_____

_____

_____

6. (*f*, *p*, or *s*) In 1972, somebody ate one _____ound of grapes (with seeds) in sixty-five seconds.

_____

_____

_____

7. (*d*, *pr*, or *t*) In 1971, Dave Man of England ate 130 _____unes in 105 seconds.

_____

_____

_____

8. (*cr*, *dr*, or *str*) The world's record for eating ice _____eam is held by a man who ate seven pounds, thirteen ounces of it in sixteen minutes.

_____

_____

_____

3 **Word Sounds.** Fill in the right word on each line. Then check your answers to make sure they make sense. Note how the first one has been done.

chairs
pair
stairs

1. The top of the __*stairs*__ was blocked by a __*pair*__ of __*chairs*__.

cloud
loud
proud

2. Dave was so _____ of the _____ he drew in art class that he said in a _____ voice, "Hey, everybody, look at my picture!"

brave
cave
waves

3. The boys tried to be _____ as the _____ came crashing into the _____.

cried
dried
tried

4. After Sue _____, she _____ to stay by herself until her tears _____.

clear
hear
near

5. Linda did not _____ her boss tell her to _____ off the desk that was _____ the front door.

change
range
strange

6. Cowboys riding on the _____ sometimes think that a _____ in the sky is _____.

beans
mean
jeans

7. The cowboy didn't _____ to spill _____ all over his _____.

bunch
lunch
munched

8. Eddie didn't have time to eat _____ on Thursday, so he _____ on a _____ of pretzels while he worked.

bricks
stick
trick

9. Jack thought there must be a _____ to getting the _____ to _____ to each other in just the right way.

cape
grape
shape

10. The _____ of the _____ made Mary's head look like a _____.

4 **Smallest and Biggest.** In each set of words, which is the smallest? Write the answer on the line to the left. Which is the biggest? Write the answer on the line to the right. Note how the first set has been done.

Smallest   **Biggest**

second   1. hour, minute, or second   _hour_

_____   2. day, month, or week   _____

_____   3. city, country, or state   _____

_____   4. hundred, million, or thousand   _____

_____   5. human being, monkey, or shrimp   _____

_____   6. pint, ounce, or quart   _____

_____   7. gallon, pint, or quart   _____

_____   8. lamp, light bulb, or sun   _____

_____   9. bike, ship, or truck   _____

_____   10. pork chop, roast beef, or shrimp   _____

_____   11. chestnut, rose, or tree   _____

_____   12. Rome, United States, world   _____

5 **Word Opposites.** Match each word at the left with the word that means the opposite. Note how the first one has been done.

always   _clear_   1. cloudy
anger
brand-new   _____   2. cute
change
children   _____   3. joy
√clear   _____   4. men and women
grew   _____   5. never
saved   _____   6. shrank
sea
ugly   _____   7. sky

          _____   8. spent

          _____   9. stay the same

          _____   10. used

Lesson 5

Love Letters

Words for Study

letter	paper	well-known	vowel
written	surely	fan	remember
lover	copy	either	person
scribe	John	important	preacher
easy	chain	alphabet	reason

Love Letters

The strangest love letter ever written was the work of a French painter in 1875. The only thing written in the letter was "I love you." What is strange about the letter is that "I love you" was written 1,875,000 times—a thousand times the year of the date!

The lover did not write this letter himself. He hired a scribe to do it for him. A scribe is a person who writes letters and other things for a living.

This painter didn't just tell the scribe he had hired to write a letter saying "I love you" 1,875,000 times and then go off to paint. This would have been too easy.

Instead, the lover stayed right there with the scribe and said "I love you" 1,875,000 times. Each time he said it, the scribe had to write these three words down on paper. Surely, this must have been the most boring job that this scribe ever had!

Used by permission of Ripley International Ltd. © 1944

1 About the Reading. Answer these questions.

1. In what year did the French painter hire somebody to write a love letter for him? _____

2. What is a person hired to write or copy something for somebody else called? _____

3. How many times did the scribe have to write "I love you" on paper? _____

4. If you were the French painter and you hired a scribe to write this letter in 1984, how many times would he have to write "I love you"? _____

What do you think?

5. What do you think the woman who got this letter thought of her lover?

_____

6. Give a reason that explains why people wrote more letters in the 1800's than they write today.

_____

2 Word Sounds. Choose the right word and fill it in on the line.

selling
spelling
telling

1. A letter that a woman writes to a man _____ him that she no longer loves him is called a "Dear John" letter.

classed
massed
passed

2. A letter that is copied and then _____ on to someone else to read is called a chain letter.

mail
pail
rail

3. Letters that well-known people get from those who really like their work are called fan _____.

knife
life
wife

4. A red-letter day is a day that has been either a very happy day or a very important day in your _____.

fix
mix
six

5. There are twenty-_____ letters in the English alphabet.

bore
more
store

6. The letter *e* is used _____ often than any other letter of the alphabet.

towels
vowels

7. *A, E, I, O,* and *U* are called _____.

much
such

8. In English, there is no _____ thing as a word without a vowel sound in it.

skill
spill
still

9. Can you _____ sing the song that you learned as a child to help you remember all the letters of the alphabet?

long
song
wrong

10. The _____ sounds like this: "A, B, C, D, E, F, G. H, I, J, K, L, M, N, O, P.   Q, R, S, T, U, V.   W, X, Y, and Z. Now I've said my A B C's. Tell me what you think of me."

3   **Who Does What?** Choose the right answer at the left and write it on the line. Note how the first one has been done.

baseball player
√cab driver
clown
cowboy
doctor
painter
preacher
scribe
tailor
teacher

1. A _*cab driver*_ drives people where they want to go.

2. A _____ gets base hits.

3. A _____ helps people to learn.

4. A _____ helps people who are sick.

5. A _____ herds cows on the range.

6. A _____ makes and mends clothes.

7. A _____ makes people laugh.

8. A _____ paints pictures.

9. A _____ tells people about the teachings in the Bible.

10. A _____ writes letters for other people.

4 **Words That Sound the Same.** Put the right word on each line.

right *and* write

1. Bob could not _____ with his _____ hand after he had smashed it in the car door.

hole *and* whole

2. The dog ran off with the _____ bone and hid it in a _____ behind the house.

beat *and* beet

3. The mother _____ the dust from the bed until her face got as red as a _____ .

fair *and* fare

4. The people did not think that the new bus _____ was _____ .

meat *and* meet

5. The women would _____ each other on the street and talk for hours about the high price of _____ .

heard *and* herd

6. The cowboy said, "Have you _____ that the _____ will sell for a higher price this year?"

sails *and* sale

7. Ben read in the paper that there was a _____ on _____ at the boat shop down at the dock.

one *and* won

8. It was the middle of June, and Bucky's team had not _____ _____ baseball game yet.

5 **Marking Vowels.** Mark the vowels in these words either long or short. If you don't hear the vowel at all, draw a line through it.

1. frām€	4. pint	7. tend	10. spend
2. brănd	5. cave	8. mass	11. spice
3. own	6. grin	9. trick	12. throne

Review: Lessons 1-5

Say these words out loud.

charm	chart	smart	smoke	choke	check
drew	draw	straw	stroke	broke	break
germ	term	team	steam	stain	chain
purr	puff	stuff	step	stop	chop
skirt	skill	shrill	shrink	shrunk	skunk
slang	sleep	creep	crumb	thumb	numb

ail	band	cheek	bend	brick	blink	blown
pail	brand	peek	lend	lick	drink	grown
rail	land	seek	mend	pick	ink	known
sail	grand	week	spend	stick	sink	own
tail	stand		tend	trick	stink	

1 **Choosing the Answer.** Choose the right word and fill it in on the line.

1. There are _____ states in the United States.
   (a) forty   (b) forty-nine   (c) fifty   (d) fifty-two

2. The speaker gave a _____ on Rome that lasted for more than an hour.
   (a) tail   (b) tale   (c) talk   (d) tall

3. Dave couldn't make any _____ out of the words Linda had written on the paper.
   (a) send   (b) sense   (c) sent   (d) seen

4. Joan would never buy blouses that had too much _____ on them because they were too hard to take care of.
   (a) lace   (b) lake   (c) lame   (d) lane

5. After seven years of married life, Bucky was still very much in love with his _____.
   (a) made   (b) make   (c) male   (d) mate

6. John said that he hadn't _____ to hurt the child's feelings.
   (a) mean   (b) meant   (c) meat   (d) met

7. When Kate returned from lunch, she had a huge _____ of ketchup on her brand-new blouse.
   (a) blob   (b) bob   (c) mob   (d) sob

8. When the robber pointed a gun at Kate, she was sure he was _____.
   (a) bleeding   (b) blessing   (c) bluffing   (d) blushing

9. Louise didn't remember to _____ her book, so she had to pay a small fine.
   (a) react   (b) refund   (c) refuse   (d) renew

10. As Bob drank the water from the pond, he told June, "Don't make such a fuss. The water is not _____."
    (a) deadly   (b) loudly   (c) strongly   (d) surely

2 **Number Words.** Answer these questions by writing the word for the number. Get a friend to help you if you wish. Some of these questions are hard!

_____ 1. How many days are in a week?

_____ 2. How many weeks are in a year?

_____ 3. How many ounces are in a pound?

_____ 4. How many ounces are in a cup?

_____ 5. How many cups are in a pint?

_____ 6. How many pints are in a quart?

_____ 7. How many quarts are in a gallon?

_____ 8. How many stripes are in the United States flag?

_____ 9. How many stars are on the United States flag?

_____ 10. According to some people, how many years of bad luck will you have if you break a mirror?

_____ 11. How many years ago did the _Mayflower_ land on the New England coast?

_____ 12. What is one hundred times ten?

3 **Facts.** List the five senses.

1. _____

2. _____

3. _____

4. _____

5. _____

Word Index: Lessons 1-5

A
alphabet
anger
animal
away

B
Bible
blink
blob
blown
bluff
brand
brand-new
break
brew
brick
bunch

C
catbird
catcall
catfish
catty
cave
chain
change
chart
cheek
chestnut
children
chin
choke
Clark
cloud
cloudy
copy
country
cover
cowboy
creep

D
deadly
describe
dim
doctor
drank
draw
drink
dust

E
easy
Egypt
eighty
either
England
English
every

F
fan
fifty
fold
frame
further

G
gallon
grand
grew
grin
grown

H
has
human
hundred

I
important
instead
its

J
January
John

K
kill

L
leave
letter
lover

M
mass
Mayflower
meaning
meant
mirror
mouth
munch

N
New England
noise

O
own

P
pail
paper
period
person
Pinocchio
pint
pound
preacher
pub
puff
purr

Q
quart

R
rail
react
reading
reason
record
remember
renew
Rome

S
sail
scribe
scroll
sea
seal
second
sense
seventh
seventy
shape
shrill
sin
size
slang
smoker
snob
somebody
someone
sometimes
speaker
spell
spend
spent
spice
state
stew
stick
stink
strongly

sunlight
surely
swell

T
tailor
tend
term
thousand
throne
touch
towel
trick

U
ugly
United States

V
vowel

W
well-known
world
written

X

Y

Z

Lesson 6

Wigs

Doreen Yarwood, illustrations from *The Encyclopedia of World Costume*. Copyright © 1979 Doreen Yarwood. Reprinted with the permission of Atheneum Publishers, Inc.

Words for Study

bigwigs	wool	early	floated
B.C.	bee	under	cure
shaved	wax	queen	hangover
lice	France	Anne	compound

Wigs

Have you ever heard a very important person called a *bigwig*? This term dates back to at least 4000 B.C. At that time, both men and women in Egypt shaved their heads and wore wigs. The bigger the wig was, the more important the person was.

One of the reasons that wigs were worn in Egypt was so people could keep their heads clean and free from lice. The wigs were made of many things such as wool, animal hair, and even gold. People used bee's wax to make the wigs stick to their heads.

It was not just the people in Egypt who liked to wear wigs. In 1624, when the king of France began to lose his hair at a very early age, he got everybody to wear wigs. Under Queen Anne of England, who ruled from 1702 to 1714, wigs grew to their biggest shapes. They covered people's backs and floated down over their chests.

Adapted and reprinted with permission from *Hair: The Long and Short of It* by Bill Severn, 1971. Published by David McKay, Co., Inc.

1 **About the Reading.** Answer these questions.

1. Name three things the people in Egypt used to make their wigs.

   _____   _____   _____

2. What did the people in Egypt use to make their wigs stick to their heads?

   _____

3. Why did the king of France in this story start to wear a wig?

   _____

4. Describe the wigs that were worn during Queen Anne's time.

   _____

5. How many years did Queen Anne rule England? _____

6. How did the term *bigwig* get started?

   _____

What do you think?

7. Do people still fuss as much with their hair now as they did a long time ago?
   Be sure to give a reason for your answer.

   _____

   _____

2 **Word Sounds.** Choose the right word and fill it in on the line.

brave
grave
shave

1. When people _____ their heads, they are bald.

bangs
fangs
gangs

2. Mary had her _____ cut so she could see better.

chair
hair
pair

3. Most wigs that are worn today look just like human _____.

rich
which
witch

4. There are many sayings in _____ the word *hair* is used.

feeling
kneeling
peeling

5. _____ really relaxed is called "letting one's hair down."

fighting
lighting
sighting

6. _____ with somebody over something that is not very important is called "splitting hairs."

bugs
dug
hugs

7. When somebody _____ you, he is "getting in your hair."

grand
sand
stand

8. If something really scares you, it "makes your hair _____ on end."

cares
scares
stares

9. If something really _____ you, and you don't react at all, you "do not turn a hair."

brakes
flakes
takes

10. The "hair of the dog that bit one" is a drink a person _____ to try to cure a hangover.

3 **Which Word Does Not Fit?** Put the word that does not fit with the rest on the line to the right. Note how the first one has been done.

1. January	June	May	month	*month*
2. England	English	France	United States	_____
3. catbird	catfish	eel	whale	_____
4. ink	paper	pen	scribe	_____
5. cloud	kite	start	sun	_____
6. Andy	Anne	Jack	John	_____
7. chair	queen	seat	throne	_____
8. cheek	chin	mouth	wrist	_____
9. ailing	cure	ill	sick	_____
10. gallon	pint	pound	quart	_____

4 **Vowel Sounds.** If the sound for *ea* in the word is long, put the word in the first list. If the sound for *ea* is short, put the word in the second list. Note how the first one has been done.

√bean
beat
bread
breakfast
dead
easy
instead
please
squeak
sweat

Long Sound for *ea*	**Short Sound for *ea***
1. _____bean_____	1. _____
2. _____	2. _____
3. _____	3. _____
4. _____	4. _____
5. _____	5. _____

5 **Compound Words.** A compound word is made up of two or more smaller words. Find the two words that make up each compound word and write them on the lines. Note how the first one has been done.

1. bathroom _____bath_____ + _____room_____

2. bigwig _____ + _____

3. breakfast _____ + _____

4. catbird _____ + _____

5. checkbook _____ + _____

6. everything _____ + _____

7. gingerbread _____ + _____

8. girlfriend _____ + _____

9. shortstop _____ + _____

10. sunburn _____ + _____

Lesson 7

Skunks

USDA

Words for Study

bloodstream	he's	snaps	straight
breath	whatever	shoots	trouble
pouches	stamp	six-shooter	formed
liquid	forefeet	rounds	coins
hidden	raised	sideways	shower

Skunks

A skunk's bad smell is not part of his bloodstream or his breath. Under the skunk's tail are two pouches which are filled with liquid. These pouches remain hidden as long as everything is calm. However, when the skunk feels he's in danger, these pouches come out.

A skunk will not spray the liquid in these pouches unless he feels he's being chased. If chased, the first thing a skunk will do is turn to face whatever is chasing him. Then he stamps his forefeet and raises all of his tail but the white tip. If the skunk feels he's still in danger, he raises the white tip, snaps his tail into the shape of the letter U, and shoots.

The skunk can fire the liquid from a range of ten to twelve feet. This liquid can be smelled for more than a mile. Like a six-shooter, each of the pouches has enough liquid for six rounds. A skunk can fire his liquid sideways, straight, and up with no trouble at all. After he fires all his liquid, the skunk has to wait a week before more liquid is formed.

1 **About the Reading.** Answer these questions.

1. Where does the liquid that a skunk sprays come from?

   _____

2. From what range can a skunk spray his liquid?

   _____

3. After the skunk sprays his liquid, how long must he wait before he can spray again?

   _____

4. Why does a skunk spray his liquid?

   _____

5. When a skunk feels he's in danger, list three things that he does.

   a. _____

   b. _____

   c. _____

Do you know?

6. If your pet or you are sprayed by a skunk, how do you get rid of the smell?

   _____

2 **Words That Mean the Same.** Match each word at the left with the word that has the same meaning. Note how the first one has been done.

bluff   _____*munch*_____   1. chew
creep
dim   _____   2. covered
form
friendly   _____   3. crawl
hidden
√munch   _____   4. dark

sprint   _____   5. dash
touch
trouble   _____   6. feel

           _____   7. fool

           _____   8. kind

           _____   9. problems

           _____   10. shape

3 **Word Opposites.** Match each word at the left with the word that has the opposite meaning. Note how the first one has been done.

√a nobody   _a nobody_   1. a bigwig
find
forget   _____   2. early
hard   _____   3. easy
late
lovely   _____   4. everything
nothing
saved   _____   5. float
sink   _____   6. kneel
stand
    _____   7. lose

    _____   8. remember

    _____   9. spent

    _____   10. ugly

4 **Compound Words.** Find the two words that make up each compound word and write them on the lines.

1. bedroom   _____ + _____

2. bloodstream   _____ + _____

3. cowboy   _____ + _____

4. homework   _____ + _____

5. *Mayflower*   _____ + _____

6. notebook   _____ + _____

7. sideways   _____ + _____

8. someone   _____ + _____

9. sunlight   _____ + _____

10. whatever   _____ + _____

5 **Silly Verses.** Choose the right word from each set of five words and fill it in on the line.

cry
dates
sky
state
straight

1. A cowboy who lives in our _____

    Is well-known for shooting so _____.

    He shoots coins from the _____.

    It makes the girls _____.

    They beg him to take them on _____.

cried
dance
France
pants
tried

2. There once was a king of _____,

    Who couldn't fit into his _____.

    He tried and he _____,

    Then he broke down and _____.

    He couldn't even go to the _____.

hour
life
shower
sour
wife

3. When everything seems to turn _____,

    John waits for a better _____.

    He gives thanks for his _____,

    For his kids and his _____,

    And then goes to take a hot _____.

Lesson 8

Eggs

USDA

Words for Study

clutch	grow	fought	Easter
hatch	chick	chicken	worth
within	peep	weigh	chocolate
bird	against	double	basket
sister	shell	yolk	sentence

Eggs

Would a talking egg surprise you? Think of the fact that most eggs are laid at one time, and a clutch of them might hatch during one week. It is important that they hatch within a few hours of each other so the last baby bird to come out will not be killed by his much older and bigger brothers and sisters.

For this reason, the eggs must time their hatching. This is done by talking egg to egg and often, egg to mother and mother to egg. For a day or two before the egg hatches, some air gets into it, and the growing chick starts to make peeping sounds and pecks against the shell. Since the eggs in a nest touch each other, the sounds are heard by the others.

People have long fought over the question: "Which came first, the chicken or the egg?" The man who wrote these facts about talking eggs thinks that the egg came first. However, the first book of the Bible states that the chicken came first. What do you think?

Adapted with permission from July, 1978 *Reader's Digest.*
Copyright © 1978 by the Reader's Digest Association Inc. "The Incredible Edible Egg" by Jack Denton Scott.

1 **About the Reading.** Answer these questions.

1. Why is it important for eggs from the same nest to hatch within a short period of time?

_____

2. Why do chicks start peeping before they hatch?

_____

3. What has to happen before the baby chick can start peeping and pecking against the shell?

_____

4. In this story, who thinks that the chicken came first?

_____

5. In this story, who thinks that the egg came first?

_____

6. What do you think the word *clutch* means as it is used in this story?

_____

Do you know?

7. Can you give another meaning for the word *clutch*?

_____

2 Word Sounds. Choose the right answer and fill it in on the line. Then write all three words at the left. Check your answer to make sure it makes sense.

1. (*l*, *p*, or *s*)   The highest rate of egg _____aying by a hen is 361 eggs
in 364 days.

_____

_____

_____

2. (*sh*, *sm*, or *sp*)   The biggest egg recorded weighed sixteen ounces and

_____   had a double yolk and double _____ell.

_____

_____

3. (*p*, *r*, or *s*)   The biggest Easter egg ever made weighed 550 _____ounds
and was worth $500 in chocolate alone.

_____

_____

_____

4. (*b*, *k*, or *wh*)   Babies can eat the yolks of eggs before they can eat

_____   the _____ite part.

_____

_____

5. (*cl*, *r*, or *th*)   In January, 1970, a man ate sixteen _____aw eggs
with their shells in three minutes and twenty seconds.

_____

_____

_____

6. (*f*, *m*, or *p*)

The saying, "to lay an egg," means to _____ail at something.

_____

_____

_____

7. (*b*, *d*, or *j*)

To "put all your eggs in one basket" is to risk everything you have on _____ust one thing.

_____

_____

_____

8. (*b*, *l*, or *sp*)

A person who _____ends a lot of time reading books is sometimes called an "egghead."

_____

_____

_____

9. (*c*, *gl*, or *sc*)

A person who acts _____ared a lot is sometimes called a "chicken."

_____

_____

_____

10. (*h*, *p*, or *scr*)

Somebody who counts a lot on something that may not even happen is said to be "counting his chickens before they _____atch."

_____

_____

_____

3 **Which Word Fits Best?** Choose the word which fits best and write it on the line. Note how the first one has been done.

1. Meat is to plate as milk is to __*glass*__.
   (a) glass   (b) jug   (c) liquid   (d) white

2. Ship is to sea as plane is to _____.
   (a) fast   (b) land   (c) sky   (d) wings

3. Bread is to loaf as cigarettes are to _____.
   (a) can   (b) jar   (c) pack   (d) smoke

4. Smart is to dumb as calm is to _____.
   (a) mood   (b) relaxed   (c) sleeping   (d) upset

5. French is to France as English is to _____.
   (a) Egypt   (b) England   (c) reading   (d) school

6. March is to month as _____ is to day.
   (a) hour   (b) January   (c) Wednesday   (d) week

7. Shower is to bathroom as _____ is to living room.
   (a) armchair   (b) door   (c) light bulb   (d) sink

8. Hand is to arm as _____ is to leg.
   (a) arm   (b) body   (c) foot   (d) knee

9. Church is to pray as _____ is to learn.
   (a) books   (b) class   (c) reading   (d) school

10. Mouth is to food as _____ is to air.
    (a) body   (b) blood   (c) breath   (d) lung

4 Compound Words.
Choose a word in **List A** and add a word from **List B** to it to make a compound word. Note how the first one has been done.

List A	List B
√baby	bow
copy	cat
hand	down
hide	name
life	out
neck	√sit
nick	tie
rain	time
touch	watch
wrist	writing

1. _babysit_
2. _____
3. _____
4. _____
5. _____
6. _____
7. _____
8. _____
9. _____
10. _____

Put the compound words you have written in these sentences. Note how the compound word *babysit* has been used.

1. A _____ in football is worth six points.

2. John couldn't find a _____ to match the shirt he planned to wear to the party Saturday night.

3. Joan checked her _____ to see what time it was.

4. When the police found the robber's _____, they shouted, "Come out with your hands up."

5. Dick called his sister a _____ because she tried to do everything he did.

6. The teacher refused to read Dave's work because his _____ was so messy.

7. The mother needed someone to _babysit_ her children.

8. Do you have a _____, or do people call you by the name your father and mother gave you?

9. Do you think there is a pot of gold at the end of the _____?

10. When the Joneses won a trip to Rome, Dan said, "Wow, this is the chance of a _____!"

5 **Word Sounds.** Here are some words which have a double *o* in them. Read the words at the left and put them where they should go. Use the sound *oo* in the word at the top of each list to help you. Note how the first word has been done.

√foot
groom
hood
pool
shoot
spoon
took
tooth
wood
wool

Book

1. ___*foot*___

2. _____

3. _____

4. _____

5. _____

School

1. _____

2. _____

3. _____

4. _____

5. _____

Lesson 9

Gold

Words for Study

California	forty-niners	boot	Jesus
Sutter	wherever	El Dorado	golden
news	knee-deep	common	whatsoever
miner	lonely	isn't	ye
dollars	shacks	glitters	truth

Gold

In January, 1848, gold was found in California. The gold was found on land owned by John A. Sutter. He tried very hard to keep the good news hushed up, but by May miners were streaming in.

A few men found between 300 and 500 dollars worth of gold dust a day. However, most of the miners panned one ounce of gold dust each day, which was worth about twenty dollars. Since workers back East were making only a dollar a day then, twenty dollars was a lot of money to these men.

The real gold rush began in 1849 when 100,000 men from all over the world rushed to California to strike it rich. These men were called the "forty-niners." They lived in mining camps which formed wherever somebody had made a strike. These camps had only one street that was deep in dust during the dry spells and knee-deep in mud when the rains came.

Men would work hard all day digging for gold and then return to their lonely shacks at night to fix a meal of beans, fried bread, and coffee. It was so rare to see a woman in one of these towns that men would pay a dollar just to look at a pair of women's boots.

1 About the Reading. Answer these questions.

1. In which state did the gold rush happen? _____

2. On what man's land was the gold first found? _____

3. In what year did the real gold rush begin? _____

4. What were the men called who came to California
to strike it rich? _____

5. How many ounces of gold dust did most of the miners find
each day? _____

6. Why would men pay a dollar just to stare at a pair of women's boots?

_____

What do you think?

7. If you had been living in 1849, would you have rushed to California
to find gold? Explain your answer.

_____

_____

2 **Word Sounds.** Pick the right answer and fill it in on the line. Then write all three words at the left. Check your answer to make sure it makes sense.

1. (*br, d,* or *spr*)

_____

_____

_____

In the 1500's, a story _____ead about a land rich in gold that was called El Dorado.

2. (*b, f,* or *th*)

_____

_____

_____

People _____ought that gold was as common as sand in El Dorado.

3. (*bl, f,* or *m*)

_____

_____

_____

Through the years, many men set out to _____ind El Dorado, and they often thought they had found it.

4. (*f, c,* or *p*)

_____

_____

_____

Gold that looks just like gold, but isn't gold at all is called

_____*ool's gold.*

5. (*l, cl,* or *m*)

_____

_____

_____

Do you know what this saying _____eans: "All that glitters is not gold "?

6. (*b, s,* or *sp*)

_____

_____

_____

Pay dirt is a term used to describe _____oil that is rich enough so that lots of money can be made from mining.

7. (b, pr, or r)   Jesus _____eached the Golden Rule, which is "All things
                      whatsoever ye would that men should do to you, do ye
_____   even so to them."

_____

_____

8. (l, sn, or sp)   If a person _____eaks the truth, we say that "his word is
                      as good as gold."
_____

_____

_____

3   **Vowels + the Letter l.** Use the words at the left to fill in the lines
        in the sentences.

bald   1. A _____ helps to keep your pants up.
bell
belt   2. Are you short or _____?
bulb
cold   3. Little children are told to "let the ball _____" when it goes
gold   into the street.
hill
Jill   4. Many children are told to drink four glasses of _____ a day.
milk
roll   5. Men in 1849 looked for _____ in California.
tall
wall   6. The light _____ was the wrong size for the lamp.

          7. The pictures hanging on the _____ were lovely.

          8. When the _____ rang, everybody came in for lunch.

          9. When you have a bad _____, you sneeze a lot.

          10. When you have no hair on your head, you are _____.

          11. Jack and _____ went up the _____ to fetch a pail of water.

4 Marking the Vowels. Mark the vowels that have lines under them. Note how the first two words have been done.

1. līcé
2. egghĕad
3. wax
4. within
5. float
6. reason

7. raise
8. grave
9. knee-deep
10. nest
11. France
12. brake

13. between
14. just
15. hatch
16. tip
17. since
18. weak

5 Matching. Match each word at the left with the words that best describe it.

bigwig
chocolate
coffee
hangover
kneel
lice
March
news
peach
yolk

_____ 1. a hot, strong, black liquid

_____ 2. a food that grows on trees

_____ 3. a sweet used in candy or drinks

_____ 4. a very important person

_____ 5. the main part of an egg

_____ 6. the third month of the year

_____ 7. to get down on your knees

_____ 8. very small bugs that bite the skin of people and animals

_____ 9. what you see on television or read in the paper

_____ 10. what a person has the morning after drinking the night before

Lesson 10

Mother Goose

Randolph Caldecott, Courtesy of Penguin Books Ltd.

Words for Study

goose	proof	lady	fiddler
though	rhymes	soup	shut
claim	example	diddle	elm
graveyard	tease	sport	guide
Boston	fiddle	stuck	silent

Mother Goose

Mother Goose was not a real person even though some people claim that she really lived. In an old graveyard in Boston, there are many graves bearing the name of Goose. Some people think that one of these graves belongs to Mother Goose, but there is no proof that this is really so.

One of the earliest Mother Goose books of rhymes and stories for children was printed in 1760. Many of these rhymes had been around for hundreds of years before they were called Mother Goose rhymes. Some of the rhymes have no real meaning, but others tell about real people.

For example, one queen of England loved to tease her lords the way a cat plays with mice. She also loved to dance to tunes played on a fiddle. One of her lords was nicknamed "Moon," and another lord was known as the Queen's "lap dog."

This queen never ate her soup without having one of her ladies-in-waiting, called 'Spoon," taste the soup first. The man who carried the soup was called "Dish." When the "Dish" and the "Spoon" ran off to get married one day, somebody in the queen's court made up this rhyme:

> Hey diddle, diddle,
> The cat and the fiddle,
> The cow jumped over the moon;
> The little dog laughed
> To see such sport
> And the dish ran away with the spoon.

1 **About the Reading.** Answer these questions.

1. In what city in the United States do some people think Mother Goose lived? _____

2. In what year was an early Mother Goose book printed? _____

3. Do all the rhymes tell about real people? _____

4. What was the "Dish's" job? _____

5. What was the "Spoon's" job? _____

6. What happened to the "Dish" and the "Spoon"?

_____

7. What fact in the story tells us that Mother Goose did not write these rhymes shortly before 1760?

_____

What do you think?

8. Why do children like to hear Mother Goose rhymes?

_____

_____

2 **Word Sounds.** Can you end these lines from well-known rhymes? Pick the right answer and fill it in on the line.   Then write all three words at the left. (Get a friend to help if you do not remember all the rhymes.)

1. (*b*, *c*, or *h*)   Little Boy Blue come blow your ＿＿＿orn.

＿＿＿＿＿＿

＿＿＿＿＿＿

＿＿＿＿＿＿

2. (*d*, *p*, or *t*)   Four and twenty blackbirds baked in a ＿＿＿ie.

＿＿＿＿＿＿

＿＿＿＿＿＿

＿＿＿＿＿＿

3. (*cl*, *n*, or *r*)   There came a little blackbird and nipped off her ＿＿＿ose.

＿＿＿＿＿＿

＿＿＿＿＿＿

＿＿＿＿＿＿

4. (*b*, *f*, or *r*)   She whipped them all soundly and put them to ＿＿＿ed.

＿＿＿＿＿＿

＿＿＿＿＿＿

＿＿＿＿＿＿

5. (*f*, *sh*, or *str*)   And Tom went crying down the ＿＿＿eet.

＿＿＿＿＿＿

＿＿＿＿＿＿

＿＿＿＿＿＿

6. (*bl*, *cl*, or *sh*)   The mouse ran up the ＿＿＿ock.

＿＿＿＿＿＿

＿＿＿＿＿＿

＿＿＿＿＿＿

7. (*d, p,* or *fl*)   Three, four, shut the _____oor.

   _____

   _____

   _____

8. (*fr, thr,* or *tr*)   And he called for his fiddlers _____ee.

   _____

   _____

   _____

9. (*c, cr,* or *l*)   And one for the little boy that lives in the _____ane.

   _____

   _____

   _____

10. (*dr, pl,* or *sl*)   He stuck in his thumb and pulled out a _____um.

   _____

   _____

   _____

3 **Which Word Does Not Fit?** Use the first word as a guide word to help you choose the word in the line that does not fit. Note how the first one has been done.

1. **country:**	California	Egypt	France	United States	_California_
2. **summer:**	beach	snow	sunburns	tans	_____
3. **month:**	January	March	May	spring	_____
4. **time:**	hour	minute	pound	second	_____
5. **Christmas:**	cards	eggs	gifts	Jesus	_____
6. **trees:**	chestnut	elm	leaves	pine	_____
7. **liquids:**	ice	soup	water	wine	_____
8. **drinks:**	beer	coffee	straw	tea	_____
9. **body:**	air	chest	lungs	spleen	_____
10. **clothes:**	blouse	jeans	vest	wool	_____
11. **women:**	cowboys	ladies	queens	sisters	_____
12. **job:**	doctor	miner	smoker	tailor	_____
13. **water:**	beach	lake	pond	sea	_____
14. **baseball:**	base	bat	bunt	punt	_____

4 **Silent Letters.** In each of these words, there is one letter that you do not hear. This is called a silent letter. Write the word on the line. Then draw a line through the silent letter. Note how the first one has been done.

1. knit _Knit_   5. wrong _____   9. meant _____

2. breath _____   6. thumb _____   10. heart _____

3. clutch _____   7. wrist _____   11. lamb _____

4. crane _____   8. climb _____   12. watch _____

5 **Words That Sound the Same.** Put the right word on each line.

read *and* red

1. Dick sat in his _____ armchair and _____ his book until his wife came home from the meeting.

sea *and* see

2. The people ran for the seats on the top deck, so they could _____ the _____ better.

weak *and* week

3. Jill was still so _____ that she took another _____ off from work to rest.

threw *and* through

4. Mack wanted to get _____ with his work as fast as he could so he really _____ himself into it.

bare *and* bear

5. When the hunters returned to camp, they knew that a _____ had been there because the food chest was _____.

way *and* weigh

6. "By the _____," said Eddie, "did you remember to _____ yourself today?"

brake *and* break

7. "It will _____ Nick's heart when he hears that one _____ on his brand-new bike doesn't work at all," said his sister.

cents *and* sense

8. "It doesn't make any _____ to spend sixty _____ on a candy bar," said Louise.

Review: Lessons 1-10

Say these words out loud. (A few of the words are new, but if you use the rules you have learned, you will have no trouble with them.)

shave	share	dare	dart	chart	chick
clutch	Dutch	ditch	switch	swipe	pipe
claw	thaw	thin	grin	grow	flow
paint	pint	point	joint	join	coin
swell	smell	smile	while	wheat	heat
drove	stove	starve	carve	cart	smart

ail	clap	beep	bleach	dim	book	boil	bunch
bail	map	creep	peach	him	look	coil	crunch
jail	slap	jeep	preach	Jim	took	oil	hunch
hail	snap	peep	reach	slim	crook	soil	munch
sail	trap	sheep	teach	trim	crooked	spoil	punch

1 Choosing the Answer. Choose the right word and fill it in on the line.

1. Tom was sleeping so _____ that he didn't hear the noise from the party next door.
   (a) deadly   (b) hardly   (c) soundly   (d) surely

2. Even _____ Mary had enough money to buy the dress, she decided not to get it after all.
   (a) though   (b) thought   (c) through   (d) threw

3. "It's a _____ that the city doesn't plan better housing for the people who live in the slums," said Jack.
   (a) shake   (b) shame   (c) shape   (d) share

4. The ducks quacked and the chickens _____ as the fox broke through the wire.
   (a) peeked   (b) peeled   (c) peeped   (d) peered

5. After Jim fed the baby, he patted her back to help her _____.
   (a) burn   (b) burp   (c) burst   (d) bust

6. Bob thought it was a _____ that June wasted so much money on cigarettes.
   (a) sin   (b) sip   (c) sit   (d) six

7. The _____ reason that Joan didn't do the dishes right away was that she wanted to watch the six o'clock news.
   (a) maid   (b) mail   (c) main   (d) many

8. "If you tell my wife what I bought her for her birthday, you will _____ all my fun," said Nick.
   (a) soil   (b) spell   (c) spill   (d) spoil

9. Mary didn't know the answer to the teacher's question, but she took a wild _____ anyway.
   (a) guess   (b) guest   (c) guide   (d) guilt

10. She had a _____ that it was the wrong answer.
    (a) bunch   (b) hunch   (c) munch   (d) punch

2 **Words That Mean the Same.** Match each word at the left with the word that has the same meaning.

brake   _____   1. close
break
dirt   _____   2. gleam
during
glitter   _____   3. kid
guide
melt   _____   4. lead
rhyme
shut   _____   5. rot
slim
spoil   _____   6. shatter
tease
               _____   7. soil

               _____   8. stop

               _____   9. thaw

               _____   10. thin

               _____   11. verse

               _____   12. while

3 **Word Opposites.** Match each word at the left with the word that has the opposite meaning.

against   _____   1. birth
cloudy
crooked   _____   2. clear
death
evening   _____   3. common
forgot
lies   _____   4. for
messy
rare   _____   5. freeze
shut
thaw   _____   6. morning
weak
               _____   7. neat

               _____   8. open

               _____   9. remembered

               _____   10. straight

               _____   11. strong

               _____   12. truth

60   Review: Lessons 1-10

Word Index: Lessons 1-10

A
against
alphabet
anger
animal
Ann(e)
away

B
babysit
bail
basket
B.C.
bee
belong
Bible
bigwig
bird
blackbird
blink
blob
bloodstream
blown
bluff
boot
Boston
bought
brake
brand
brand-new
break
breath
brew
brick
bunch
bust

C
California
catbird
catcall
catfish
catty
cave
chain
change
chart
cheek
chestnut
chick
chicken
children
chin
chocolate
choke
claim
Clark
claw

cloud
cloudy
clutch
coil
coin
common
compound
copy
copycat
country
cover
cowboy
crane
creep
crook
crooked
crunch
cure

D
deadly
describe
diddle
dim
doctor
doesn't
dollar
double
drank
draw
drink
dust

E
early
Easter
easy
egghead
Egypt
eighty
either
El Dorado
elm
England
English
every
example

F
fan
fiddle
fiddler
fifty
float
fold
forefeet
forgot
form
forty-niner

fought
frame
France
further

G
gallon
gang
glitter
goes
golden
goose
grand
grave
graveyard
grew
grin
grow
grown
guide

H
hail
handwriting
hangover
has
hatch
he's
hidden
hideout
human
hunch
hundred

I
important
instead
isn't
its

J
January
Jesus
Jill
Jim
John

K
kill
knee-deep
kneel

L
lady
leave
letter
lice
lifetime
liquid
lonely
lover

M
March
mass
May
Mayflower
meaning
meant
miner
mirror
mouth
munch

N
necktie
nest
New England
news
nickname
nip
noise

O
own

P
pail
paper
peach
peep
period
person
Pinocchio
pint
pipe
pouch
pound
preach
preacher
proof
pub
puff
punch
purr

Q
quart
queen

R
rail
rainbow
raise
react
reading
reason
record
remember
renew
rhyme

Rome
round

S
sail
scribe
scroll
sea
seal
second
sense
sentence
seventh
seventy
shack
shape
shave
sheep
shell
shoot
shower
shrill
shut
sideways
silent
sin
sister
six-shooter
size
slang
slim
slum
smoker
snap
snob
soil
somebody
someone
sometimes
soundly
soup
speaker
spell
spend
spent
spice
spoil
sport
spread
stamp
stare
state
stew
stick
stink
stove
straight

strongly
stuck
sunlight
surely
Sutter, J.
swell

T
tailor
tease
tend
term
thaw
though
thousand
throne
tip
touch
touchdown
towel
trap
trick
trim
trouble
truth

U
ugly
under
United States

V
vowel

W
wax
weak
weigh
well-known
whatever
whatsoever
wherever
within
wool
world
worth
wristwatch
written

X

Y
ye
yolk

Z

Lesson 11

Sleeping

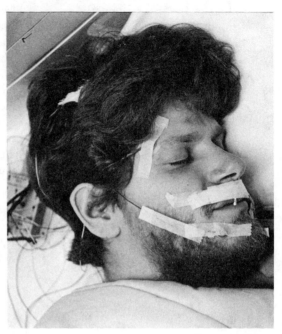

A man helps doctors in a lab learn about sleep.

Scripps Clinic and Research Foundation

Words for Study

sleepy	move	fins	lawn
yawn	brings	winter	chessboard
asleep	fourth	crack	pawns
become	log	dawn	lawful
breathing	choice	mow	awful

Sleeping

On most nights, as you start to get sleepy, you may yawn a few times. Yawning is a very common way in which your body tries to draw in more air.

After you go to bed, changes start to happen in your body even before you fall asleep. Your body heat goes down, and your brain waves become more even. When you do fall asleep, your heart rate slows down, your body relaxes, and your breathing becomes very even.

Doctors say that we move through four stages of sleep each night. Each stage brings us into deeper sleep. On most nights, we go through these stages four or five times.

Most dreaming takes place during the fourth stage, which is called REM. REM sleep lasts from five to twenty minutes at a time. During REM sleep, the body is so limp that if anybody tried to wake you up, you would not be able to move for quite a few seconds.

People do not sleep "like a log." We move in our sleep as many as twenty to forty-five times every night. Much of this turning happens when our bodies are moving from one stage of sleep into the next. If we did not move at all during the time that we sleep, we could become quite sick.

1 **About the Reading.** Answer these questions.

1. Why do we yawn when we are sleepy?

_____

2. List two changes that happen in the body *before* you even fall asleep.

   a. _____

   b. _____

3. List three changes that happen in the body *after* you fall asleep.

   a. _____

   b. _____

   c. _____

4. During what stage does most dreaming happen?

_____

5. What would you do if somebody woke you up during this stage?

_____

6. What would happen to your body if you did sleep "like a log"?

_____

What do you think?

7. Why do you think people dream?

_____

8. Do you tend to remember most of your dreams, or do you forget them as soon as you wake up?

_____

2 **Word Sounds.** Here are some words with *aw* in them. Use the words at the left to fill in the lines with the right answers. Note how the first one has been done.

awful
claws
dawn
jaw
law
lawful
lawn
pawns
✓paws
straw
thaws
yawn

1. People have hands; dogs have __*paws*__.

   Fish have fins; birds have _____.

2. In the winter it freezes; in spring, the ice _____.

   You eat meat with a fork and sip Coke through a _____.

3. Last night, the boxer broke his _____.

   As a rule, fighting's against the _____.

4. The lady got up at the crack of _____.

   She raked the leaves and mowed the _____.

5. The second row on a chessboard is lined with _____.

   If you're bored with chess, you tend to _____.

6. Smoking in lobbies is often not _____.

   I hope you don't think this work is too _____.

3 **Long and Short Vowels.** Put the right words on the lines.

breath
breathe

1. John's necktie was so tight that he could hardly _____.

   Sue had been running so hard that she had trouble catching

   her _____.

bath
bathe

2. Bucky always took a shower in the morning, but his wife liked

   to _____ just before dinner.

   The king took his _____ in a tub made of gold.

tap
tape

3. Do you ever _____ your foot when you feel upset?

Linda couldn't remember where she left the roll of _____.

scrap
scrape

4. Ben threw his dog a _____ of ham that was left over from breakfast.

It took Joan all afternoon to _____ the paint off the ceiling.

grip
gripe

5. Andy liked to _____ about taxes even though he had no choice but to pay them.

When Dave lost his _____ on the rope, he fell into the water.

twin
twine

6. Ann had not seen her _____ sister since she moved to California.

The cat got her paw twisted up in the ball of _____.

4 **Putting Words in Order.** Put the words in order so that each sentence makes sense.

1. Clark   couldn't   go   Mr.   sleep   to

_____

2. counting   first   he   sheep   tried

_____

3. a   cup   fixed   he   himself   of   tea   then

_____

4. asleep   couldn't   fall   he   still

_____

5. day   fired   for   he   job   next   on   sleeping   the   the   was

_____

Lesson 12

Honeybees

USDA

Words for Study

honey	young	unmated	nectar
honeybee	drones	allowed	shot
build	guard	flowers	busy
hives	sting	empty	sly

Honeybees

There are 10,000 kinds of bees in the world. However, only honeybees make honey and wax that people can use. There are three classes of honeybees:

1. the queen, which lays the eggs
2. the workers, which build the hives, get the food, and care for the young
3. the drones, which mate with the queen

Laying eggs is the queen's only job. The workers feed her and care for her. The queen honeybee does not rule the hive, but the workers get very upset if she is not there. Like the queen, all the workers are female. However, the workers are smaller than the queen.

A worker returning to the hive from a food hunt does a "dance" to tell the other workers where the food is. Some workers do not hunt for food because they always stand guard at the hive. All the bees in any one hive have their own smell. They can tell if a stranger is near because it doesn't smell the same.

And what are the drones, or male honeybees, doing all this time? Nothing. They do no work and have no sting. The drones' only job is to mate with a young queen. An unmated queen can lay only drone eggs. She must be mated to have worker eggs.

In the fall when the honey flow is over, the workers let the drones starve to death. They are no longer useful and would eat too much of the stored honey if they were allowed to live.

Source material for this article: *World Book Encyclopedia*

1 **About the Reading.** Answer these questions.

1. How many kinds of bees are there in the world? _____

2. List the three classes of honeybees and what they do.

Class	**Job**
a. _____	_____
b. _____	_____
c. _____	_____

3. Which two classes of honeybees are female?

_____ and _____

4. What kind of eggs does an unmated queen lay? _____

5. What kind of eggs does a mated queen lay? _____

6. At what time of the year is the honey flow over? _____

7. Why are drones useful?

_____

8. What happens to the drones when they are no longer useful?

_____

9. What would happen if a hive had no drones?

_____

2 **Word Sounds.** Choose the right answer and fill it in on the line. Then write all three words at the left. Check your answer to make sure it makes sense.

1. (*br, gl,* or *l*)   Flowers have _____ands that make nectar.

_____

_____

_____

2. (*b, s,* or *t*)   The worker honeybees _____uck up nectar from the flowers.

_____

_____

_____

3. (*d, f,* or *h*)   Then the bee returns to the _____ive and sucks the nectar back through its mouth.

_____

_____

_____

4. (*g* or *l*)   It either _____ives the nectar to the other bees or puts it into an empty cell of the hive.

_____

_____

_____

5. (*fl, sh,* or *tr*)   Bees _____y about twelve miles an hour.

_____

_____

_____

6. (*gr, p,* or *r*)   A worker honeybee gets enough nectar in her lifetime to make about $1/10$ of a _____ound of honey.

_____

_____

_____

7. (*h* or *m*)   To make one pound of _____oney, all the bees' flying time would add up to 13,000 miles.

_____

_____

_____

8. (*Dr*, *P*, or *Sk*)   _____unks often eat the worker bees.

_____

_____

_____

3 **Words That End in -y.** Add -*y* to these words.
Study the examples before you begin.

1. sleep + y = *sleepy*

2. water + y = _____

3. stick + y = _____

4. corn + y = _____

5. creep + y = _____

6. worth + y = _____

1. spice + y = *spicy*

2. shine + y = _____

3. noise + y = _____

4. bounce + y = _____

5. flake + y = _____

6. wave + y = _____

1. sun + y = *sunny*

2. snap + y = _____

3. pig + y = _____

4. kit + y = _____

5. bud + y = _____

6. fog + y = _____

4 **Words That End in -ly.** Use the words at the left for these sentences. Study the example before you begin.

barely
bravely
√brotherly
calmly
cheaply
commonly
lonely
nearly
sharply
weekly

1. The Bible teaches us much about __*brotherly*__ love.

2. When Linda heard strange sounds coming from the living room, she didn't get upset. She just picked up the phone

   and _____ called the police.

3. The speaker for the evening was pleased to see that the room

   was _____ full and that everybody seemed quite happy to be there.

4. Bucky made the right turn too _____ and nearly crashed into the parked car.

5. The little boy smiled _____ as the doctor rolled up his sleeve to give him the shot.

6. When the car broke down on Monday, Joan had no idea how

   she was going to do her _____ shopping.

7. Eddie got home so late from work that he _____ had enough time to eat before he had to leave again.

8. When Jill's youngest child left home, the house seemed

   very _____ for a long time.

9. Ms. Bond liked to do her shopping downtown because she could buy

   her clothes more _____ there.

10. It is a sad fact, but rats are _____ found living in the slums.

5 **Common Sayings.** Can you end these common sayings? Choose the right word at the left for each saying.

bat
bee
beet
fox
gold
kite
lark
sheet
snail
the nose on your face

1. as blind as a _____

2. as busy as a _____

3. as good as _____

4. as happy as a _____

5. as plain as _____

6. as red as a _____

7. as slow as a _____

8. as sly as a _____

9. as white as a _____

10. higher than a _____

Lesson 13

Handwriting

Words for Study

studying	upon	present	downhill
expert	factors	tomorrow	drag
employer	slant	uphill	large
certain	up-and-down	bright	whose

Handwriting

Everything we do tells other people something about who we are. Some people think that they can learn a lot about us by studying our handwriting. Sometimes these people hire handwriting experts. For example, an employer might hire a handwriting expert to tell him if a certain person would be the right one for a job. Sometimes the police call upon handwriting experts to work with them on certain cases.

There are at least sixteen factors that a handwriting expert looks at when he studies handwriting. One factor is the slant of the letters. An up-and-down slant shows that the writer lives in the present and is ruled by his head. A right slant shows that the writer lives for tomorrow and goes by the rules that other people have made. A left slant shows that the writer lives in the past, doesn't always go by the rules, and tends to keep to himself.

A second factor in studying handwriting is how the writing line goes. If the writer's lines tend to go uphill, he is a person who looks on the bright side of things. If the writing line goes downhill, the person is often sad and thinks life is a drag.

A third factor in studying handwriting is to note how big and wide the letters are. Large letters tell us that the person would really like to make something out of his life. Round letters show that the person can roll with the punches. Wide letters show a person who will let others see his feelings. However, letters that are not wide at all show a person who won't let others see who he really is.

1 About the Reading. Answer these questions.

1. List three of the main factors that a handwriting expert looks at when he studies handwriting.

a. _____

b. _____

c. _____

2. True or false? Read each sentence. If the sentence is true according to what you have just read, write *true* on the line to the left. If the sentence is false according to what you have just read, write *false* on the line to the left.

_____ a. A person who writes with an up-and-down slant lives for tomorrow.

_____ b. A person who slants his letters to the left lives in the past.

_____ c. A person whose writing line goes uphill looks on the bright side of things.

_____ d. A person whose writing line goes downhill looks on the bright side of things.

_____ e. Large letters show that the person can roll with the punches.

_____ f. A person whose letters are not wide at all does not let others see his feelings.

Just for Fun

3. Write your full name in the box.

```

```

Study your handwriting and answer these questions according to what you have just read.

a. Do you think you live in the present, tomorrow, or the past?

_____

b. Do you think you look at the bright side of things, or do you think life is a drag?

_____

c. Do you think you would likc to make something of your life?

_____

d. Do you think you let others see your feelings, or do you tend to hide them?

_____

What do you think?

4. Do you think handwriting experts can tell us something about who we really are?

_____

5. Based on your study of your own handwriting, would you want to change it, or do you like it just the way it is?

_____

2   **Words That Mean the Same.** Match each word at the left with the word that has the same meaning.

allow
barely   _____   1. boss
bright   _____   2. big
certain   _____   3. hardly
double
employer   _____   4. let
large   _____   5. shiny
marry
present   _____   6. sure
scream

_____   7. today

_____   8. twice

_____   9. wed

_____   10. yell

3 **Word Opposites.** Match each word at the left with the word that means the opposite.

asleep   _____   1. awake

begin

birth   _____   2. cloudy

bright   _____   3. death

summer

sunny   _____   4. downhill

uphill   _____   5. dull

won

yesterday   _____   6. end

young

           _____   7. lost

           _____   8. old

           _____   9. tomorrow

           _____   10. winter

4 **Vowel Sounds.** Say the words at the left out loud. Then say the guide words out loud. Put the words under the guide words that have the same vowel sound. Study the example before you begin.

√are	**Star**	**Air**	**Ear**
bear			
beer	1. _are_	1. _____	1. _____
carve			
dear	2. _____	2. _____	2. _____
deer			
fair	3. _____	3. _____	3. _____
hard			
heart	4. _____	4. _____	4. _____
here			
march	5. _____	5. _____	5. _____
peer			
stare			
their			
wear			

Lesson 14

To Be a Slave

Words for Study

slave	background	rivers	July
freedom	themselves	washed	whenever
ex-slave	kept	overdone	business
war	flood	bathtub	table
nowhere	fields	wouldn't	group

To Be a Slave

Most of us dream about having freedom to do anything we want. In dreaming about freedom, we sometimes forget that we need certain things before we can really love being free.

Many ex-slaves have recorded the stories of their lives. These stories help us to know more about what freedom means. Here is the story of how one ex-slave saw life for her people just after the slaves were set free in 1863 during the War Between the States.

Slaves prayed for freedom. When they got it, they didn't know what to do with it. They were turned out with nowhere to go and nothing to live on. They had no background in looking out for themselves. They had nothing to work with and no land.

They made me think of the crowd one time who prayed for rain when it was dry in crop time. The rain fell and kept falling until there was almost a flood. The fields were so wet that you could not go in them. Water was standing in the fields in the middle of every row. The ditches in the fields looked like little rivers because they were so full of water.

Then one of the men who had been praying for rain looked up and said, "I tell you, brothers, if it doesn't quit raining, everything is going to be washed away." They all looked at the black rain cloud in the west with sad faces as if they felt they didn't know what use they had for rain after they had gotten it.

Then another brother said, "Brothers, don't you think we have overdone this thing?"

That's what many a slave thought about praying for freedom. It was bad to be a slave, and freedom of the kind we got with nothing to live on was bad too.

From *To Be a Slave*, copyright ©1968 by Julius Lester. Adapted and reprinted by permission of the publisher, Dial Books for Young Readers, a Division of E.P. Dutton, Inc.

1 **About the Reading.** Answer these questions.

1. In what year did the slaves in the United States get their freedom? _____

2. List four factors that made it hard for slaves to deal with their new freedom.

   a. _____

   b. _____

   c. _____

   d. _____

3. Why does the woman who is telling the story say that the ex-slaves remind her of the crowd that prayed for rain?

   _____

   _____

What do you think?

4. Describe something you feel you need that can help you really love your freedom.

   _____

   _____

2 **Choosing the Right Heading.** Choose the right heading for each group of words. Study the example before you begin.

√Baseball
Christmas
Farms
Games
Lights
School
Snacks
Soups
War
Water

_____ _____ **_Baseball_** _____ _____ _____

animals	batter	bean	bombs
barn	catcher	chicken	fighting
crops	manager	egg drop	guns
fields	mitts	split pea	tanks

_____ _____ _____ _____

bridge	classes	flares	cards
checkers	homework	lamps	Jesus' birthday
chess	notebooks	lighters	presents
poker	tests	matches	Yule logs

_____ _____

fudge	lakes
mints	ponds
popcorn	streams
pretzels	rivers

3 **Words That End in -er.** Add -er to these words. Study the examples before you begin.

1. stick + er = _sticker_

2. hang + er = _____

3. heat + er = _____

4. crack + er = _____

5. mow + er = _____

1. mine + er = _miner_

2. dive + er = _____

3. make + er = _____

4. dance + er = _____

5. freeze + er = _____

1. trap + er = _trapper_

2. bat + er = _____

3. dip + er = _____

4. zip + er = _____

5. swim + er = _____

4 More Words That End in *er.* Use the words at the left for these sentences. Study the example before you begin.

campers
checkers
✓coaster
corner
dresser
folder
lighter
poker
rubber
slippers

1. Joan asked Eddie to please put a ___coaster___ under his glass, so it wouldn't make a ring on the table.

2. Dan started to lend Andy his comb, but then he remembered he had left it on the _____ in his bedroom.

3. Dave kept all his art work in a large, brown _____.

4. Sue bought a _____ mat for the bathtub, so her children wouldn't slip in the tub and hurt themselves.

5. The _____ hoped that it wouldn't rain during the Fourth of July weekend.

6. The first thing Louise did when she got home from work was change her clothes and put on her _____.

7. The store on the _____ of Fourth and Main Streets is going out of business next month.

8. When Linda quit smoking, she gave away her cigarette _____.

9. When Mack raised Jack's bet in the _____ game, everybody thought he was bluffing.

10. Whenever Kate was asked to babysit at Mary's house, they would spend the evening playing _____.

5 **Putting Sentences in Order.** Read the five sentences. Then write them in order so they make sense. (These sentences are from another story by an ex-slave.)

— A white man was there who was very rich and mean and owned many slaves.

— "If you bid for me, I will take a knife and cut myself from ear to ear before I would be owned by you."

— He was so mean that many white and black people hated him.

— When I was fifteen years old, I was put up on the block for sale.

— When he bid for me, I talked right out on the block.

1. _____

_____

2. _____

_____

3. _____

_____

4. _____

_____

5. _____

_____

Lesson 15

A Very Strange Hobby

Kathryn Raymond

Karl Hunziker

Rubadeau/Kissinger

Words for Study

hobby	barbed	swizzle	helicopter
brink	reported	hooked	fence
snagged	sold	link	cutters
above	gold-plated	strand	order

A Very Strange Hobby

Have you ever heard any of these names: Hold Fast, Saw Tooth, Wrap Around, Brink Twist, or Necktie? If not, then you haven't been snagged by one of the strangest hobbies in the United States. All of the names listed above are kinds of barbed wire that have been made in the United States since 1867.

What do you do with barbed wire after you get it? Well, one man is reported to have sold 4,000 gold-plated, barbed wire swizzle sticks to a big store. At last report, every one of these swizzle sticks had been snapped up for eight dollars a set.

Not all people sell their barbed wire. As one barbed wire fan says, "I'm hooked on barbed wire because it's a link to this country's past. Barbed wire is one of the things that won the West."

The main goal of people who love barbed wire is to own at least one strand of every kind of barbed wire ever made. However, this can't be done because some kinds of barbed wire are no longer around. After all, how could people living in 1867 have known that the people living today would be so crazy about barbed wire? Strands of barbed wire that are very rare have sold for as much as thirty to forty dollars a strand.

One man, who is a doctor, is so stuck on barbed wire that he hunts for old barbed wire by helicopter. In his spare time, he spends hours flying over miles of fences that are no longer used. Whenever he sights something that looks good, he sets his helicopter down in a field, takes out a pair of wire cutters and snags off a strand or two of barbed wire.

Adapted with permission from *Incredible Collectors, Weird Antiques and Odd Hobbies* by Bill Carmichael.© 1971 by William E. Carmichael. Published by Prentice-Hall, Inc. Englewood Cliffs, NJ 07632.

1 **About the Reading.** Answer these questions.

1. List three brand names of barbed wire.

   _____   _____   _____

2. Describe how one man made a lot of money with his barbed wire.

   _____

3. What is the main goal of barbed wire fans?

   _____

   _____

4. Put what the doctor does in looking for barbed wire in the right order.

   He flies over miles of fence looking for barbed wire.
   He sets his helicopter down in a field.
   He sees something that looks good.
   He takes out his wire cutters and snips off a strand.
   The doctor gets into his helicopter.

   a. _____

   b. _____

   c. _____

   d. _____

   e. _____

5. The kinds of barbed wire were most likely named for _____

   _____

   a. the people who first made them.   c. the town where they were first made.
   b. the way they looked.   d. the way they were used.

What do you think?

6. The people who most likely used barbed wire in 1867 were _____

   a. doctors.   c. cattlemen.
   b. farmers.   d. outlaws.

7. Why did these people use it? _____

   _____

2 **Working with Words That Rhyme.** Say the words at the left out loud. Then put each word on the right line so the sentences make sense.

cold
folded
gold
sold

1. It was too _____ to look for _____, so the men

_____ up their tents, _____ their tools, and headed south.

brink
drink
sink
stink

2. Whenever Ms. Parks had a bad cold, she felt she was at the

_____ of death. As she got a _____ of water from

the _____, she could tell (even though her nose was stopped up)

that the pile of dishes was beginning to _____.

bent
rent
tent
went

3. The pole for the _____ was so _____ that Billy _____

over to his friend's store to see if he could _____ a better one
for the camping trip.

lacked
Mack
rack
sack

4. _____ wanted to buy all the chocolate candy bars on the

_____, but he _____ a _____ to carry them all home in.

bare
cared
share
spare

5. Bucky's wife _____ a lot about other people and wanted to

_____ what she had, but her own house was so _____

that she wasn't able to _____ very much.

butter
cutters
Sutter
utter

6. Mr. _____ didn't _____ a word when his crazy wife used

wire _____ to spread _____ on her toast.

luck
stuck
sucked
tucked

7. After Jill _____ the baby in her crib, the baby _____ her

thumb into her mouth, _____ it for a few minutes, and fell

fast asleep. "What good _____!" thought Jill.

bring
king
sing
sting

8. The _____ asked his lord to _____ something for his

bee _____ and then _____ him a song to calm his nerves.

griped
ripe
swiped
wiped

9. As Mr. Lane _____ the table, he _____ to the diner

that somebody had _____ all the _____ peaches from the box in the back room.

book
crook
hook
look

10. When the _____ gave the policeman a mean _____,

the policeman said, "You're not going to get off the _____, Bud.

We're going to throw the _____ at you."

3 **How Do You Say It?** Choose the right word at the left and write it on the line. Study the example before you begin.

bar
batch
book
bunch
can
deck
✓flock
herd
load
loaf
pack
pair
pot
quart
school

1. a _flock_ of birds

2. a _____ of bread

3. a _____ of cards

4. a _____ of cigarettes

5. a _____ of coffee

6. a _____ of cows

7. a _____ of fish

8. a _____ of fudge

9. a _____ of grapes

10. a _____ of milk

11. a _____ of pants

12. a _____ of peas

13. a _____ of soap

14. a _____ of stories

15. a _____ of wash

Review: Lessons 1-15

> **Say these words out loud.** (A few of the words are new, but if you use the rules you have learned, you will have no trouble with them.)
>
> | | | | | | | | |
> |---|---|---|---|---|---|---|---|
> | plain | ash | bleed | click | bold | couch | blue | bust |
> | rain | cash | deed | kick | cold | crouch | clue | crust |
> | Spain | dash | greed | stick | fold | grouch | due | dust |
> | sprain | flash | seed | tick | sold | ouch | glue | must |
> | stain | trash | weed | trick | told | pouch | Sue | rust |

1   **Choosing the Answer.** Choose the right word and put it on the line.

1. Glue can make your hands very _____.
   (a) shiny   (b) snappy   (c) sorry   (d) sticky

2. Everybody liked Louise's pies because her crusts were so _____.
   (a) bouncy   (b) flaky   (c) sticky   (d) watery

3. When it is very _____, drivers can see better using their dim lights instead of their bright lights.
   (a) clear   (b) cloudy   (c) foggy   (d) sunny

4. Ms. Bond _____ her car loan in three years.
   (a) recorded   (b) refunded   (c) repaid   (d) reported

5. It took the woman a long time to find the folder because she had _____ it in the wrong place.
   (a) filed   (b) filled   (c) filmed   (d) firmed

6. When a black cat _____ your path, do you feel you're going to have bad luck?
   (a) bosses   (b) crosses   (c) losses   (d) tosses

7. Kitty was all dressed up and had _____ to go.
   (a) nobody   (b) no one   (c) nothing   (d) nowhere

8. So many people are such _____ in the morning until they have had their first cup of coffee.

   (a) couches (b) crouches (c) grouches (d) pouches

9. Kate added two cups of nuts to the cake _____ before she poured it into the baking pan.

   (a) batter (b) better (c) bitter (d) butter

10. At the sale, the duke _____ three thousand dollars on the painting of the English queen.

    (a) bad (b) bed (c) bid (d) bud

11. Joan bought a jar of honey for herself and a jar of _____ jam for her aunt.

    (a) grape (b) grip (c) gripe (d) group

12. Which of these bees have no sting? _____

    (a) drones (b) queens (c) workers

13. The _____ is the day this country celebrates claiming its freedom from England.

    (a) Christmas (b) Easter (c) Fourth of July (d) New Year's Day

14. The War Between the States was between the _____.

    (a) employers and workers   (c) North and South
    (b) East and West   (d) slaves and free people

2 **Silent Letters.** In each of these words, there are one or two silent letters. Write each word on the line. Then draw a line through the silent letters. Study the example before you begin.

1. wrote ~~w~~rot~~e~~   7. knee _____

2. dumb _____   8. dodge _____

3. badge _____   9. batch _____

4. Dutch _____   10. writer _____

5. young _____   11. witch _____

6. build _____   12. certain _____

3 **Matching.** Choose the right word at the left for each sentence.

alphabet
fence
mower
oven
pepper
piggy
rainbow
stamp
towel
wax

1. If you want a pot of gold, look for the end of the _____.

2. If you want to bake cupcakes, use an _____.

3. If you want to cut the grass, use a lawn _____.

4. If you want to dry your hands, use a _____.

5. If you want to keep others out of your yard, build a _____.

6. If you want to mail a letter, you need a _____.

7. If you want to find numbers in the phone book faster, learn

the _____.

8. If you want to save your change, put your coins in a _____ bank.

9. If you want your floors to be shiny, use some floor _____.

10. If you want your food to taste spicy, use more _____.

4 **Word Sounds.** Say the words in each line out loud. Find the word in which the underlined letter or letters do not make the same sound as they do in the other words in that line. Write the odd word on the line to the right. Study the example before you begin.

1. h<u>o</u>se	n<u>o</u>se	r<u>o</u>se	wh<u>o</u>se	*whose*
2. <u>c</u>ave	<u>c</u>ertain	<u>c</u>ode	<u>c</u>ousin	_____
3. all<u>ow</u>	gr<u>ow</u>	m<u>ow</u>	rainb<u>ow</u>	_____
4. b<u>a</u>th	b<u>a</u>the	scr<u>a</u>pe	t<u>a</u>pe	_____
5. c<u>ou</u>nt	<u>ou</u>ch	s<u>ou</u>nd	s<u>ou</u>p	_____
6. ch<u>ea</u>ply	h<u>ea</u>ding	h<u>ea</u>ter	w<u>ea</u>k	_____
7. b<u>oo</u>t	fl<u>oo</u>d	pr<u>oo</u>f	sh<u>oo</u>t	_____
8. <u>g</u>inger	<u>g</u>oods	<u>g</u>oose	<u>g</u>uard	_____

5 **Compound Words.** Use a word from **List A** and add a word from **List B** to it to make a compound word for each sentence. Study the example before you begin.

List A

ash
baby
busy
cheese
fire
✓lip
over
stage
sun
under

List B

body
cake
coach
crackers
done
glasses
line
sitter
✓stick
tray

1. If a woman wants her lips to look red, she uses

   lipstick.

2. If you want to go out for the evening, hire

   a _____ to look after your children.

3. If the sun is too bright for your eyes, wear

   _____.

4. If a smoker needs something for his ashes, he uses

   an _____.

5. If you want to make lots of noise on the Fourth of July,

   get some _____.

6. If you hate to eat steak that is _____, order it rare
   when you go out to eat.

7. When people went from city to city in the West a long time

   ago, they rode on a _____.

8. If you care about how much you weigh, stay away from

   _____.

9. If you want to remember an important rule in your

   notebook, _____ it.

10. If you want to know everything that's happening on your

    block, ask a _____.

Word Index: Lessons 1-15

A
above
against
allow
alphabet
anger
animal
Ann(e)
ash
ashtray
asleep
away
awful

B
babysit
babysitter
background
bail
barbed
barely
basket
bathe
bathtub
batter
B.C.
become
bee
belong
Bible
bid
bigwig
bird
bitter
blackbird
blink
blob
bloodstream
blown
bluff
bold
boot
Boston
bought
bouncy
brake
brand
brand-new
bravely
break
breath
breathe
brew
brick
bright

bring
brink
brotherly
buddy
build
bunch
business
bust
busy
busybody

C
California
camper
catbird
catcall
catfish
catty
cave
certain
chain
change
chart
cheaply
checker(s)
cheek
cheesecake
chessboard
chestnut
chick
chicken
children
chin
chocolate
choice
choke
claim
Clark
claw
click
cloud
cloudy
clue
clutch
coaster
coil
coin
common
commonly
compound
copy
copycat
corner
corny
couch

country
cover
cowboy
crack
cracker
crane
creep
creepy
crook
crooked
crouch
crunch
crust
cure
cutters

D
dancer
dawn
deadly
deed
describe
diddle
dim
dipper
diver
doctor
doesn't
dollar
double
downhill
drag
drank
draw
dresser
drink
drone
drunk
dust

E
early
Easter
easy
egghead
Egypt
eighty
either
El Dorado
elm
employer
empty
England
English
every
example

expert
ex-slave

F
factor
fan
fence
fiddle
fiddler
field
fifty
fin
firecracker
flaky
flash
float
flood
flower
foggy
fold
folder
forefeet
forgot
form
forty-niner
fought
fourth
Fourth of July
frame
France
freedom
freezer
further

G
gallon
gang
glitter
goes
golden
gold-plated
goods
goose
grand
grave
graveyard
greed
grew
grin
grip
gripe
grouch
group
grow
grown

guard
guide

H
hail
handwriting
hanger
hangover
has
hatch
heading
heater
helicopter
he's
hidden
hideout
hive
hobby
hook
honey
honeybee
human
hunch
hundred

I
important
instead
isn't
its

J
January
Jesus
Jill
Jim
John
July

K
kept
kill
kitty
knee-deep
kneel

L
lady
large
lawful
lawn
leave
letter
lice
lifetime
lighter
link
lipstick

liquid
log
lonely
lover

M
maker
March
mass
May
Mayflower
meaning
meant
miner
mirror
mouth
move
mow
mower
munch

N
nearly
necktie
nectar
nest
New England
news
New Year's Day
nickname
nip
noise
noisy
no one
nowhere

O
order
ouch
overdone
own

P
pail
paper
pawn
peach
peep
period
person
piggy
Pinocchio
pint
pipe
poker
policeman
pouch

pound
preach
preacher
present
proof
pub
puff
punch
punk
purr

Q
quart
queen

R
rail
rainbow
raise
react
reading
reason
record
remember
renew
report
rhyme
river
Rome
round
rubber
rust

S
sail
scrap
scrape
scribe
scroll
sea
seal
second
sense
sentence
seventh
seventy
shack
shape
sharply
shave
sheep
sheet
shell
shiny
shoot
shot
shower
shrill
shut
shy
sideways
silent
sin
sister
sitter

six-shooter
size
slang
slant
slave
sleepy
slim
slipper
slum
sly
smoker
snag
snap
snappy
snip
snob
soil
sold
somebody
someone
sometimes
soundly
soup
Spain
speaker
spell
spend
spent
spice
spicy
spoil
sport

spread
stagecoach
stamp
stare
state
stew
stick
sticker
sticky
sting
stink
stove
straight
strand
strongly
stuck
study
suck
sunlight
sunny
surely
Sutter, J.
swell
swimmer
swizzle

T
table
tailor
tape
tease
tend
term

thaw
themselves
though
thousand
throne
tip
tomorrow
toss
touch
touchdown
towel
trap
trapper
trash
trick
trim
trouble
truth
tuck
twine

U
ugly
under
underline
United States
unmated
up-and-down
uphill
upon
utter

V
vowel

W
war
wash
watery
wavy
wax
weak
weigh
well-known
whatever
whatsoever
whenever
wherever
whose
winter
within
wool
world
worth
worthy
wouldn't
wristwatch
written

X

Y
yawn
ye
yolk
young

Z
zipper

Lesson 16

Whales

Two divers study a blue whale.

Words for Study

earth	streamlined	alive	related
hind	cold-blooded	tons	mammals
limb	warm	great	curses
gills	warm-blooded	caught	foiled
drown	temperature	stormed	broom

Whales

The whale is the largest animal that has ever lived on the earth or in the water. Millions of years ago, whales did live on land and walk on four legs. In fact, small bones that once were the whale's hind limbs are still present in the whale's body.

No one knows why whales left the land to live in the water. However, when they made the sea their home, their bodies changed in many ways. They became streamlined and shaped like a fish so they could swim faster.

But whales are not fish. A fish breathes air by means of gills and soon dies if it is kept out of water. A whale will drown, just like a human being, if it is under water too long.

Fish are cold-blooded. This means that the heat of their blood changes with the heat of the water. Whales, like land mammals, are warm-blooded. This means that the blood stays at the same temperature, no matter how cold or hot the water may become.

Fish lay eggs, but whales give birth to their young alive and nurse them with milk as do land mammals. The milk is white and looks like cow's milk. People who have tasted whale's milk claim that it is very strong and tastes awful.

Whales do not bear their young more often than every two years. In most cases, there is only one baby. However, cases of twins have been recorded. The size of the baby whale is related to the size of the mother. One writer recorded a 25-foot baby whale that weighed eight tons. The mother whale shows a great deal of love for her young and will not often leave, even if the baby is killed.

Today, the means of hunting whales works so well that whales are in danger of being killed off. It is said that there are only a few hundred thousand whales left in the whole world.

1 **About the Reading.** Answer these questions.

1. Tell how fish and whales are not at all the same in these three things.

	Fish	**Whales**
a. Breathing	_____	_____
b. Blood	_____	_____
c. Birth	_____	_____

2. What does it mean to be *cold-blooded*?

_____

3. What does it mean to be *warm-blooded*?

_____

4. True or false? Read each sentence. Write *true* on the line to the left if the sentence is true. Write *false* on the line to the left if the sentence is false.

_____ a. A whale is a mammal.

_____ b. Whales used to walk on land.

_____ c. There is no proof that whales ever walked on land.

_____ d. Whales are the largest animals that have ever lived.

_____ e. Most people like the taste of whale's milk.

_____ f. Whales bear their young every year.

_____ g. The size of a baby whale is related to the size of the mother.

_____ h. Mother whales love their babies very much.

_____ i. People no longer hunt whales.

_____ j. Whales are in danger of all being killed off.

_____ k. Whales must come to the top of the water to breathe.

What do you think?

5. What do you think should be done when any kind of animal is in danger of being killed off?

_____

_____

2 **Changing the y to i.** Study how the first set has been done. Then do the same with the remaining words.

1. busy   _busier_   _busiest_

2. noisy   _____   _____

3. happy   _____   _____

4. lucky   _____   _____

5. sleepy   _____   _____

3 **More Work with Changing the y to i.** Say the words at the left out loud. Then put them on the right lines.

busily
noisily
happily
luckily
sleepily

1. After the king and queen were married, they lived _____ ever after.

2. Sue was _____ fixing dinner when the phone rang.

3. The child sat at the table and _____ sipped his chocolate milk through a straw.

4. The lady _____ switched off the clock and went back to bed.

5. _____, Tim didn't have to work on Saturday, so he could drive his aunt to the doctor's.

4 **Silly Little Stories.** In each group of words at the left, the last letters have been changed. Say the words in each group out loud. Then fill in the words from each group on the lines, so the sentences make sense.

swear
sweat
sweater
swell

1. Jim used to _____ all the time that he wouldn't be caught dead in a _____ because they made him _____ so much. However, when Mary gave him one for his birthday, he thought it was a _____ gift.

locked
loss
lost
lot

2. Dave was so mad that he had been stood up by his date that he stormed all the way back to the parking _____. When he saw that he had _____ his keys and was _____ out of his car, he went crazy. A policeman came by, but he was at a _____ as to how he could help Dave.

dam
damp
Dan
dashed

3. A mean, mean man named Deadly _____ decided to blow up the _____. After doing this, he _____ off to his hideout in his _____ clothes. When he saw the law waiting for him at his door, he screamed, "Curses, foiled again!"

band
bang
bank
banker

4. A _____ of robbers held up the _____ on the corner of First and Wall Streets. One of the robber's guns went off with a _____, and a _____ dropped dead from the shock.

crumbs
crunched
crushed
crust

5. The man was so upset when the little old lady gave him only a _____ of bread to eat that he _____ it in his hands, threw the _____ on the floor, and _____ them under his foot.

wings
winked
wished
witch
without

6. The ugly old _____ felt lost _____ her broom. She _____ she had _____, so she could fly home. She uttered some strange words and _____ at her cat three times, but nothing happened. So there she was—stuck in the middle of the woods for the rest of her life.

5 Which Word Fits Best? For each sentence, choose the right answer from the four choices and put it on the line.

1. Herd is to cows as mob is to _____.
   (a) crowd   (b) noise   (c) people   (d) street

2. Eel is to fish as whale is to _____.
   (a) fish   (b) mammal   (c) school   (d) swim

3. Forget is to remember as lose is to _____.
   (a) find   (b) keep   (c) loss   (d) mind

4. Hive is to bees as barn is to _____.
   (a) hay   (b) horses   (c) rakes   (d) ducks

5. Elm is to tree as rose is to _____.
   (a) bud   (b) flower   (c) lovely   (d) vase

6. Bunt is to baseball as punt is to _____.
   (a) foot   (b) football   (c) fourth down   (d) kick

7. Wool is to sheep as hide is to _____.
   (a) cow   (b) dog   (c) pig   (d) ram

8. Mirror is to glass as chairs are to _____.
   (a) bricks   (b) coal   (c) glass   (d) wood

9. Before is to after as yesterday is to _____.
   (a) past   (b) present   (c) today   (d) tomorrow

10. Always is to never as often is to _____.
    (a) common   (b) hardly ever   (c) sometimes   (d) weekly

Lesson 17

Black Bart

A stagecoach
robbery in a movie

Collectors Book Store

Words for Study

Bart	middle-aged	shotgun	holdup
success	along	Charles	earned
struck	he'd	whirling	deserve
high-class	bushes	sign	cause

Black Bart (1830-1917?)

Black Bart was better at holding up stagecoaches in the Old West than any other man. He robbed stagecoaches for more than eight years before he was caught. During this period he pulled off more than thirty robberies without ever firing a shot.

There were four main reasons for Black Bart's eight years of success. He always laid careful plans. He always worked alone. He never struck near home. He always kept his plans to himself.

Black Bart, whose real first name was Charles, got his start in crime in a strange way. He was a high-class, middle-aged teacher who loved to play jokes on people. One day he was riding along the road after school when he heard the stagecoach coming down the grade. He knew the driver and thought that, just for fun, he'd give him a scare.

Black Bart hid his horse in the bushes, tied a cloth over his face, and broke a stick from a bush to use as a gun. When the stagecoach came along, he stepped out into the road and told the driver to hold up. Nobody was riding shotgun on the stagecoach, and the driver looked very scared.

"Throw out the box!" roared Black Bart.

The driver pulled the box from under the seat and tossed it out. The box just happened to land on a rock. It broke open with such a crash that Bart jumped back off the road. The driver thought that this was his chance. He laid the whip to his horses, and the stagecoach went whirling away.

In the box was the real thing—about two thousand dollars. As Bart picked it up, he thought to himself, "If I can get as much in two minutes by playing a little joke like this as I can in two years of teaching school, maybe I had better quit teaching and stick to joking."

And that's just what he did. Every time he robbed a stagecoach, he would leave behind a verse or two and sign it Black Bart P08. This is why he's known as Black Bart to this day.

Adapted from "The Case of the Plodding Highwayman or the P08 of Crime" by Ken and Pat Kraft © 1966 American Heritage Publishing Co., Inc. Reprinted by permission from *American Heritage* (December, 1966).

1 About the Reading. Answer these questions.

1. What was Black Bart's real first name? _____

2. For how many years was Black Bart a holdup man? _____

3. How many robberies did he pull off before he was caught? _____

4. How had Black Bart earned his living before he became
   a holdup man? _____

5. About how much money did Black Bart make
   in his first holdup? _____

6. Describe what Black Bart meant when he called his first holdup "a little joke."

   _____

7. List four reasons why Black Bart was so good at holding up stagecoaches.

   a. _____

   b. _____

   c. _____

   d. _____

8. Based on what Black Bart says, how much money did a teacher earn
   in the "good old days"?

   _____

What do you think?

9. Do you think it was wrong for Black Bart to rob stagecoaches?

   _____

   _____

2 **Words That Mean the Same.** Match the words at the left with the
words that have nearly the same meaning.

alive

all right

bold

cause   _____ 1. arms and legs

clue   _____ 2. brave

earn   _____ 3. deserve

high-class   _____ 4. hint

limbs   _____ 5. holdup

robbery   _____ 6. living

ton   _____ 7. okay

                       _____ 8. reason

                       _____ 9. rich

                       _____ 10. two thousand pounds

3 **Word Opposites.** Match the words at the left with their opposites.

awful   _____ 1. above

cool   _____ 2. awoke

dozed   _____ 3. bold

fresh   _____ 4. empty

froze

full   _____ 5. great

harmful   _____ 6. helpful

leave   _____ 7. remain

scared   _____ 8. stale

under   _____ 9. thawed

                       _____ 10. warm

4 **The Ending -ful.** Say the words at the left out loud. Then put them on the right lines, so the sentences make sense.

cupful
forgetful
hopeful
mouthful
sinful
spiteful
successful
thoughtful
truthful
wasteful

1. The manager told the new workers that, if they wanted to

    be _____, all they had to do was work hard.

2. Whenever Pinocchio wasn't _____, his nose grew.

3. Charles had a _____ of pretzels and could not answer June's question right away.

4. When the teacher opened the Christmas gift from her second grade

    class, she said, "Why, children, how _____ of you!"

5. Would a preacher describe Black Bart as a _____ man?

6. Jim needed one more _____ of flour to make the chocolate cheesecake.

7. Jack was so _____ that he put notes all over his house to remind himself about things he had to do.

8. The doctor was _____ that Mr. Long would be able to go back to work in one or two months.

9. Do you think it's _____ to spend money on clothes when you don't really need them?

10. A _____ person makes it his business to hurt other people's feelings.

5 **A Verse from Black Bart.** Here is an example of one of Black Bart's verses. See if you can put the words at the left on the right lines.

able
blame
bread
chance
curses
dead
hung
verses

This is my way to get money and _____.

　　When I have a _____, why should I refuse it?

I'll not need either when I'm _____,

　　And I only tax those who are _____ to lose it.

So _____ me not for what I've done,

　　I don't deserve your _____.

And if for some cause I must be _____,

　　Let it be for my _____.

Lesson 18

One Idea about How the Earth Was Formed

Words for Study

billion	heavy	solid	sponges	starfish
ocean	outer	basins	rocky	plants
universe	rim	simple	edge	seaweeds
slowly	iron	complex	worms	one-celled

One Idea about How the Earth Was Formed

Many people who study the earth claim that the earth is more than two billion years old. According to these people, the ocean is almost this old too. These people who study the earth say they can tell the age of the earth because they know the age of the rocks that make up the earth's crust. The oldest rocks that have been found are about 2.3 billion years old.

One idea about how the earth was formed is that the earth was once a ball of hot whirling gases rushing through the black spaces of the universe. Slowly this ball of flaming gases cooled. Then the gases began to turn into liquid. The matter that made up this mass became sorted out in this way:

1. Very heavy matter was in the center.
2. Less heavy matter was around the center.
3. The least heavy matter formed the outer rim.

This is still the way the earth is today, and the liquid iron that is in the center of the earth is almost as hot as it was two billion years ago.

It must have taken millions and millions of years for the outer shell of the young earth to change from a liquid to a solid state. As soon as the earth's crust cooled enough, the rains began to fall. There have never been such rains since that time. They fell day and night, days passing into months, months passing into hundreds of years. They poured into the waiting ocean basins or drained away to become seas.

As more millions of years passed, the stream of life began. At first there were only simple, one-celled forms of life. Then other life that was made up of groups of cells came into being. For example, sponges grew on the rocky floor of the sea's edge. Worms and starfish came into being. The plants were also becoming more complex. From simple, one-celled forms, there were now strange seaweeds.

During all this time, there was no life on the land. Can you picture what the land must have looked like then? No plants, no soil, no animals, no human beings—just rocks!

1   **About the Reading.** Answer these questions according to what you have just read.

1. How old is the earth?

_____

2. Why do some people who study the earth claim that the earth is this old?

_____

3. What is the heavy matter in the center of the earth?

_____

4. Did life begin in the ocean or on the land?

_____

5. Put these sentences in the order in which they happened.

The outer shell of the earth changed from liquid to solid.
Oceans and seas filled with water.
One-celled forms came into being.
The earth was a ball of hot whirling gases.
Worms and starfish came into being.
The gases began to turn into liquid form.
The rains fell.

a. _____

b. _____

c. _____

d. _____

e. _____

f. _____

g. _____

2 **Word Sounds.** Use the words at the left to fill in the answers.

sprained
sprawled
spray
sprinted

1. The young boy _____ for the house in the hope that he

could get out of the way of the skunk's _____. However, he was
running so fast that he tripped over the limb of an elm tree and was

soon _____ on the ground. The doctor told him that he

had _____ his wrist.

stranger
streets
strike
strong

2. The _____ was so _____ that everybody was very

nice when they saw him on the _____ because they were scared

he would _____ them.

swiftly
swimming
switch
swung

3. The fighter _____ so _____ that he caught the other

boxer by surprise. His head was _____ and he knew he

would have to _____ to another way of boxing just to stay in
the fight.

scraped
screamed
screen
scrubbing

4. When Charles _____ his arm on the _____ door,

   he _____ so loudly that his wife stopped _____

   the floor to go see what had happened.

square
squeezed
squirrel
squirt

5. The _____ _____ his way into the small,

   _____ box, so the skunk couldn't _____ him.

3 **The Ending -less.** Say the words at the left out loud. Then put them on the lines so the sentences make sense.

breathless
cloudless
hairless
meatless
needless
sleepless
sleeveless
thoughtless
useless
worthless

1. It was so hot on Tuesday morning that May decided to wear

   a _____ dress to work

2. Mark was so _____ after the race that he didn't even hear his friends tell him that he had won third prize.

3. Linda hoped a warm glass of milk would put an end to this

   _____ night.

4. The man at the store told the miner that what he had in his sack

   was fool's gold, which was _____.

5. Mack was so _____ that he refused to spend a dollar on a Mother's Day card.

6. During Lent, Mrs. Waters served _____ meals every Friday.

7. Tim looked at the _____ sky and knew it would be a good day for sailing.

8. The rusted knife was _____, so Bucky threw it away.

9. After he had his head shaved, Andy was shocked at the

   _____ sight that stared back at him in the mirror.

10. "_____ to say," said the teacher, "we will have homework to do for tomorrow's class."

4 **Same or Opposite?** Write *same* on the line to the left if the two words mean nearly the same thing. Write *opposite* if the two words are opposite in meaning. Study the example before you begin.

same 1. burst *and* break

_____ 2. cash *and* money

_____ 3. egghead *and* brain

_____ 4. fresh *and* stale

_____ 5. heavy *and* light

_____ 6. damp *and* wet

_____ 7. rim *and* edge

_____ 8. simple *and* complex

_____ 9. soft *and* hard

_____ 10. squeal *and* tell on

_____ 11. summer *and* winter

_____ 12. swipe *and* rob

_____ 13. thick *and* thin

_____ 14. thrill *and* bore

5 **Spelling Check.** The answers to the clues are listed at the left. As you can see, the letters of the words are all mixed up. Spell the words the right way on the lines to the right.

1. a c h M r _____ This is the third month of the year.

2. c n o r w _____ This is what the king's hat is called.

3. e e i n r s u v _____ This is another word for world.

4. k o r s t _____ Some people think this brings babies.

5. a a J n r u y _____ This is the first month of the year.

6. e e n r v _____ Some people lose this when they get scared.

7. i o n r _____ You can use this to make your clothes look neat.

8. d e o n r _____ This male honeybee does no work and has no sting.

9. a b i n o r w _____ Some people think that a pot of gold is at the end of this.

10. e e e c h s _____ This is what the rat takes in a well-known children's song.

Lesson 19

Jails on the High Seas

Mariners Museum

Words for Study

galley	battle	below	forward	everywhere
inland	mainly	flesh	thrown	one-half
remove	convicts	rise	speed	trade
wounded	hell	push	port	whom

Jails on the High Seas

Until the coming of steam, the galley was the fastest thing on the inland sea. Galleys were used to guard the coast and to remove ships that were wounded in battle. The galley was mainly an open boat for four hundred men. Who manned the oars that made the galley move so swiftly through the waters? Convicts.

Once a convict was sent to the galleys, he was no longer a man. He was an oar. He was stripped of all his clothes and put into a gang of five. Until the end of his days, he would eat, sleep, and work with the men in his gang. The men either did as they were told or were badly whipped.

When the galley was at sea, life on board was a living hell. From below deck came the awful sounds of chains, the cracking of whips on bare flesh, and screams of pain. At each oar, all five men had to rise as one on every stroke. They would push the eighteen-foot oar forward, dip it into the water, and pull with all their might. At the end of each stroke, they would drop back into their seats. Sometimes the men would row like this for twenty-four hours without a minute's rest.

Nobody ever washed. Lice were everywhere. When the convicts had to row without rest, the man carrying the whip would push rolls soaked in wine into their mouths. If a convict dropped dead or fainted, he was thrown into the sea at once.

When the galley did not have to move at full speed, the convicts could rest for one and one-half hours in every three. Also a galley spent much more time in port than at sea. When in port, the convicts (all of whom had some trade) were able to get some food from the nearest town. At night they could get some much needed sleep.

Adapted from "The Galleys of France" by W.H. Lewis in *Essays presented to Charles Williams* by permission of Oxford University Press (1947).

1 **About the Reading.** Answer these questions.

1. List two ways in which people living a long time ago used the galley.

   a. _____

   b. _____

2. If you were going to describe the galley and what life was like on the galley to a friend, list five things you would tell about it.

   a. _____

   b. _____

   c. _____

   d. _____

   e. _____

3. List three things the convicts would do when the galley was in port.

   a. _____

   b. _____

   c. _____

4. Read the first sentence. Why did people stop using the galley, and what did they use in its place?

_____

2 Words That Sound the Same. Put the right word on each line.

be *and* bee
1. The workers will _____ upset until the queen _____ returns to the hive.

know *and* no
2. I _____ of _____ better man for the job than Bart.

an *and* Ann
3. _____ had _____ hour to get all her clothes washed before she had to go to work.

throne *and* thrown
4. The king was _____ off his _____ when the bombs fell.

cent *and* sent
5. When Clark got only a one-_____ an hour raise for all the work he had been doing, he _____ his boss a letter telling him he was going to quit.

cell *and* sell
6. The man in the last _____ wanted to _____ his record so he would have money for cigarettes.

hear *and* here
7. The mother shouted, "I could _____ you better if you came in _____ to tell me what you want."

wear *and* where
8. "_____ is the new gown you plan to _____ to the party?" asked Sue's sister.

3 Which Word Does Not Fit? Choose the word that doesn't fit with the rest of the words and write it on the line to the right.

1. choose	decide	make a choice	question	_____
2. damp	dry	soaked	wet	_____
3. crowds	gangs	mobs	person	_____
4. certain	hidden	sure	true	_____
5. basin	sink	soap	tub	_____
6. dream	snore	toss and turn	work	_____

7. billions	millions	one-half	thousands	_____
8. ocean	port	river	sea	_____
9. dirt	dust	mop	scrub	_____
10. grin	gripe	look pleased	smile	_____
11. battled	boxed	bumped into	fought	_____
12. gas	liquid	solid	water	_____

4 Words That Begin with *un-*. Say the words at the left out loud. Then put them on the lines so the sentences make sense.

unable
unarmed
undress
unfair
unfolded
unfriendly
unmade
unmated
unsafe
untie

1. An _____ queen bee can lay only drone eggs.

2. The string around the box was so tight that Louise couldn't

   _____ it.

3. As the mother looked at her child's _____ bed, she just stood there, shaking her head, and said, "I give up."

4. "Don't shoot!" shouted the bank robbers to the policemen.

   "We're _____."

5. The dog chained to the pole in the Joneses' front yard looked

   so _____ that nobody ever tried to pet him.

6. Mr. Baker wouldn't let his children play outside after dark

   because he felt the streets were _____.

7. Just as Joan began to _____ for bed, she remembered she had left a cigarette burning in the ashtray on the coffee table.

8. Mike was _____ to go to the party on Saturday because he was running a temperature.

9. Andy wasn't looking forward to reading the letter from his girlfriend,

   so he _____ it very slowly.

10. When people feel down in the dumps, they tend to think that

    life is _____.

5 **Common Sayings.** Put each word at the left on the right line.

away
good
hatched
heard
heart
home
old
play
thousand
ton
will
worth

1. No news is _____ news.

2. You're only as _____ as you feel.

3. Where there's a _____, there's a way.

4. Don't count your chickens until they are _____.

5. When the cat's _____, the mice will play.

6. It hit him like a _____ of bricks.

7. All work and no _____ makes Jack a dull boy.

8. Children should be seen and not _____.

9. A bird in the hand is _____ two in the bush.

10. One picture is worth a _____ words.

11. Don't wear your _____ on your sleeve.

12. _____ is where the heart is.

Lesson 20

The Father of Our Country

The New York Historical Society

Words for Study

George	kidnap	army	sworn	everyone
Washington	plot	vice	peace	sling
February	bodyguard	angry	countrymen	slung
president	warning	New York	creak	

The Father of Our Country

The day that we call George Washington's birthday, February 22, is not really his birthday. George Washington was born on February 11. He celebrated his first nineteen birthdays on that day. In 1753, eleven days were added to the year. This change made George Washington's birthday fall eleven days later, on February 22.

Before George Washington became president of the United States, some men tried to kidnap him in order to kill him. Their plot was found out, and one of the men turned out to be Washington's bodyguard. This man was tried before the court and found guilty. On June 8, 1776, he was hanged in a field. A crowd of 20,000 people watched. Washington hoped this would serve as a warning to others who might have the same idea in mind.

Washington hated swearing. While he was in charge of the army, he sent his men an order to stop all swearing. He called swearing a "mean and low" vice. Washington told his men that God would hardly help them in the war against the English if they were always swearing at Him.

In 1782, someone told Washington that he should be king instead of president. Washington became very upset and sent the person an angry letter in which he told him never to talk like this again to anybody.

Even though George Washington was one of the richest men of his time, he had all his money tied up in land. His friends had to lend him money, so he could go to New York to be sworn in as first president of the United States.

When George Washington died ten years later, in 1799, after having served two terms as president, he was called, "First in war, first in peace, first in the hearts of his countrymen."

Adapted with permission of Joseph Kane from *Facts About the Presidents* published by Pocket Books, 1959.

1 **About the Reading.** Answer these questions.

1. What is the real date of George Washington's birth? _____

2. On what date do we celebrate George Washington's birthday? _____

3. What was the job of one of the men who tried to kidnap George Washington?

_____

4. Name the one thing that George Washington hated most. _____

5. In what city was George Washington sworn in as first president

   of the United States? _____

6. How many terms did George Washington serve as president

   of the United States? _____

7. In what year did Washington become president? _____

8. Why is George Washington called the "Father of Our Country"?

_____

Do you know?

9. How many years make up a term for a president of this country? _____

10. On which dollar bill can you see a picture of George Washington? _____

2 **Vowel Sounds.** In each group of words at the left, the vowels have been changed. Say the words in each group out loud. Then put them in the right places in the sentences.

barn
born
burned

1. Mrs. King's first baby was _____ in a _____ because their house had _____ down the night before.

crack
creaking
crook

2. When the _____ stepped on the _____ in the boards, the loud, _____ noise woke up everyone in the house.

tame
team
time

3. It took a long _____ for the cowboy to _____ the _____ of wild horses.

slammed
slim
slum

4. When the people who were working hard to clean up the _____ were told that their chances of getting any money were _____, they _____ their fists against the walls of City Hall in anger.

track
trick
truck

5. The _____ driver's _____ knee was hurting so badly that he lost all _____ of time.

slang
sling
slung

6. The stranger with his pack _____ over his back and his right arm in a _____ used so much _____ that the farmer did not know what he was talking about.

pail
peeled
pile

7. After all the paint had _____ off Jack's lunch _____, he threw it into the _____ of junk behind his house.

stars
stared
store

8. The lady stood at the door of her candy _____ for hours and _____ at the _____.

whale
wheel
while

9. _____ the man was trying to fix the steering _____ on

the boat, the _____ started to swim away.

drank
drinks
drunk

10. The boss _____ so many _____ when he threw

the birthday party for his wife that all his workers thought

he'd be _____ by nine o'clock.

3 More Work with the Ending -*ly*. Choose a word at the left
for each sentence.

badly
friendly
hardly
lovely
nearly
really
surely
swiftly

1. When John hit the Greens' fence, he _____ lost the whole
front bumper of his car.

2. "_____ Mr. Green will sue me for the price of a new fence,"
thought John to himself.

3. Even during the best of times, John and Mr. Green could

_____ be called good friends.

4. "Well, I might as well get this over with," mused John

as he walked _____ toward the Greens' front door.

5. Mr. Green's _____ wife answered the door.

6. "I _____ feel bad about what I just did to your fence,"
John began.

7. "Don't sweat it," said Mrs. Green, who was always trying to be cool.

"The fence was _____ in need of fixing up and painting anyway."

8. John hoped that Mr. Green would be as _____ about
the whole thing as his wife was.

4 **Compound Words.** Find the two little words that make up each compound word and write them on the lines to the right.

1. bodyguard _____ + _____   7. policeman _____ + _____

2. countrymen _____ + _____   8. someone _____ + _____

3. checkbook _____ + _____   9. inland _____ + _____

4. everywhere _____ + _____   10. hideout _____ + _____

5. catfish _____ + _____   11. underline _____ + _____

6. busybody _____ + _____   12. starfish _____ + _____

5 **More Common Sayings.** Choose a word at the left for each sentence.

baby
back
basket
boils
candy
easy
flies
friend
hole
pod
put
say
speak
wool

1. How time _____ when you're having fun!

2. A watched pot never _____.

3. Don't _____ all your eggs in one _____.

4. You can't pull the _____ over her eyes.

5. Everyone likes to get a pat on the _____ now and then.

6. Do as I _____ and not as I do.

7. A dog is man's best _____.

8. That was his ace in the _____.

9. Those twins look like two peas in a _____.

10. It was like taking _____ from a _____.

11. Don't _____ with your mouth full.

12. This reading book was as _____ as pie!

Review: Lessons 1-20

1 **Twenty Questions.** Use the words listed below to fill in the blanks.

alphabet	drone	galley	Pinocchio
B.C.	El Dorado	George Washington	pints
bigwig	February	Mayflower	quarts
California	forty-niners	New Year's Day	scribes
cold-blooded	Fourth of July	ounces	warm-blooded

1. The first president of the United States was _____.

2. The first president's birthday is celebrated in the month of _____.

3. On the _____, we celebrate the time this country claimed its freedom from England.

4. A ship called the _____ brought people to this country in 1620.

5. Before the coming of steam, the _____ was the fastest boat on the inland sea.

6. Long ago many people hired _____ to write letters for them.

7. Long ago men looked for _____ where they hoped to find streets of gold.

8. The state of _____ is on the west coast of the United States.

9. The _____ went to this state in the 1840's to look for gold.

10. A whale is an example of a _____ mammal.

11. An example of a _____ animal is a snake.

12. There are four _____ in a gallon.

13. There are two _____ in a quart.

14. There are sixteen _____ in a pint.

15. The _____ begins with the letter *a* and ends with the letter *z*.

16. The letters _____ are used for dates before the birth of Jesus.

17. In a well-known children's story, every time _____ told a lie, his nose grew.

18. "_____" is a slang term for a very important person.

19. A male bee is called a _____.

20. _____ is in the month of January.

2 **Words That Mean the Same.** Match each word at the left with the word that has nearly the same meaning.

bold

buddy   _____   1. almost

cause   _____   2. brave

deserve   _____   3. chew

guide   _____   4. earn

munch

nearly   _____   5. edge

present   _____   6. friend

rim   _____   7. gift

slim   _____   8. lead

utter

worthless   _____   9. reason

          _____   10. speak

          _____   11. thin

          _____   12. useless

3 **Word Opposites.** Match each word at the left with the word that has the opposite meaning.

bold   _____   1. complex

certain   _____   2. forget

crooked   _____   3. freeze

deadly   _____   4. grew

overdone

remember   _____   5. harmless

shrank   _____   6. kind

simple   _____   7. lovely

spicy

spiteful   _____   8. mild

thaw   _____   9. not sure

ugly   _____   10. rare

          _____   11. scared

          _____   12. straight

4 **Which Word Fits Best?** Choose the best answer and write it on the line.

1. Duck is to quack as chick is to _____.
   (a) peck   (b) peek   (c) peel   (d) peep

2. Second is to minute as minute is to _____.
   (a) day   (b) hour   (c) time   (d) week

3. Tea is to sip as gum is to _____.
   (a) breathe   (b) chew   (c) eat   (d) spit

4. Batter is to hitting as scribe is to _____.
   (a) pen   (b) scroll   (c) teaching   (d) writing

5. Dot is to *i* as _____ is to *t*.
   (a) cross   (b) draw   (c) print   (d) write

6. Bike is to wheels as galleys were to _____.
   (a) oars   (b) ocean   (c) steam   (d) whips

7. Mammals are to lungs as fish are to _____.
   (a) eggs   (b) fins   (c) gills   (d) warm-blooded

8. A new penny is to shiny as _____ is to noisy.
   (a) starfish   (b) copycat   (c) firecracker   (d) graveyard

9. February is to January as _____.
   (a) January is to Christmas   (c) March is to February
   (b) June is to January   (d) May is to March

10. Liquid is to solid as _____.
    (a) catfish is to water   (c) gold is to gold-plated
    (b) cream is to coffee   (d) water is to ice

5 **Words That Sound the Same.** Choose the right answer and write it on the line.

threw *or* through

1. Are you glad that you are almost _____ with this reading book?

be *or* bee

2. When the President went into the store to shake hands with the voters, his bodyguard warned him to _____ careful.

cent *or* sent

3. Charles _____ his aunt a gold-plated watch for her birthday.

weak *or* week

4. After the doctor removed the cast from his leg, George felt so _____ that he was sure he would faint.

throne *or* thrown

5. After the driver had _____ down the money box from the stagecoach, Black Bart ordered him to get moving.

board *or* bored

6. Did you feel _____ when you did your homework last night?

cents *or* sense

7. While shopping for a few new things for her bathroom, Ms. Sutter said in a loud voice, "I wouldn't give you two _____ for these ugly towels—even if they are on sale!"

way *or* weigh

8. The best time to _____ yourself is in the morning before you have had anything to eat.

brake *or* break

9. Some people have stickers on the back bumpers of their cars which read, "I _____ for animals."

know *or* no

10. Now that you are at the end of this book, do you think you _____ more about reading than you did before?

Word Index: Lessons 1-20

A
above
against
alive
allow
along
alphabet
anger
angry
animal
Ann(e)
army
ash
ashtray
asleep
away
awful

B
babysit
babysitter
background
bail
barbed
barely
Bart
basin
basket
bathe
bathtub
batter
battle
B.C.
became
become
bee
belong
below
Bible
bid
bigwig
billion
bird
bitter
blackbird
blink
blob
bloodstream
blown
bluff
bodyguard
bold
boot
Boston
bought
bouncy
brake

brand
brand-new
bravely
break
breath
breathe
breathless
brew
brick
bright
bring
brink
broom
brotherly
buddy
build
bunch
bush
busily
business
bust
busy
busybody

C
California
camper
catbird
catcall
catfish
catty
caught
cause
cave
certain
chain
change
Charles
chart
cheaply
checkers
cheek
cheesecake
chessboard
chestnut
chick
chicken
children
chin
chocolate
choice
choke
claim
Clark
claw
click
cloud

cloudless
cloudy
clue
clutch
coaster
coil
coin
cold-blooded
common
commonly
complex
compound
convict
copy
copycat
corner
corny
couch
country
countrymen
cover
cowboy
crack
cracker
crane
creak
creep
creepy
crook
crooked
crouch
crunch
crush
crust
cupful
cure
curse
cutters

D
dancer
dawn
deadly
deed
describe
deserve
diddle
dim
dipper
diver
doctor
doesn't
dollar
double
downhill
drag
drank

draw
dresser
drink
drone
drown
drunk
dust

E
early
earn
earth
Easter
easy
edge
egghead
Egypt
eighty
either
El Dorado
elm
employer
empty
England
English
every
everyone
everywhere
example
expert
ex-slave

F
factor
fan
February
fence
fiddle
fiddler
field
fifty
fin
firecracker
flaky
flash
flesh
float
flood
flower
foggy
foil
fold
folder
forefeet
forgetful
forgot
form
forty-niner

forward
fought
fourth
Fourth of July
frame
France
freedom
freezer
further

G
galley
gallon
gang
George
gill
glitter
goes
golden
gold-plated
goods
goose
grand
grave
graveyard
great
greed
grew
grin
grip
gripe
grouch
group
grow
grown
guard
guide

H
hail
hairless
handwriting
hanger
hangover
happily
has
hatch
heading
heater
heavy
he'd
helicopter
hell
he's
hidden
hideout
high-class

hind
hive
hobby
holdup
hook
honey
honeybee
hopeful
human
hunch
hundred

I
important
inland
instead
iron
isn't
its

J
January
Jesus
Jill
Jim
John
July

K
kept
kidnap
kill
kitty
knee-deep
kneel

L
lady
large
lawful
lawn
leave
Lent
letter
lice
lifetime
lighter
limb
link
lipstick
liquid
log
lonely
lover
luckily

M
mainly
maker

mammal
March
mass
May
Mayflower
meaning
meant
meatless
middle-aged
miner
mirror
mouth
mouthful
move
mow
mower
munch

N
nearly
necktie
nectar
needless
nest
New England
news
New Year's Day
New York
nickname
nip
noise
noisily
noisy
no one
nowhere

O
ocean
one-celled
one-half
order
ouch
outer
overdone
own

P
pail
paper
pawn
peace
peach
peep
period
person
piggy
Pinocchio
pint
pipe
plant
plot
poker

policeman
port
pouch
pound
preach
preacher
present
president
proof
pub
puff
punch
punk
purr
push

Q
quart
queen

R
rail
rainbow
raise
react
reading
reason
record
relate
remember
remove
renew
report
rhyme
rim
rise
river
rocky
Rome
round
rubber
rust

S
sail
scrap
scrape
scribe
scroll
sea
seal
seaweed
second
sense
sentence
seventh
seventy
shack
shape
sharply
shave

sheep
sheet
shell
shiny
shoot
shot
shotgun
shower
shrill
shut
shy
sideways
sign
silent
simple
sin
sinful
sister
sitter
six-shooter
size
slang
slant
slave
sleepily
sleepless
sleepy
sleeveless
slim
sling
slipper
slowly
slum
slung
sly
smoker
snag
snap
snappy
snip
snob
soil
sold
solid
somebody
someone
sometimes
soundly
soup
Spain
speaker
speed
spell
spend
spent
spice
spicy
spiteful
spoil
sponge

sport
spread
squirt
stagecoach
stamp
stare
starfish
state
stew
stick
sticker
sticky
sting
stink
storm
stove
straight
strand
streamline
strongly
struck
stuck
study
success
successful
suck
sunlight
sunny
surely
Sutter, J.
swell
swiftly
swimmer
swizzle
sworn

T
table
tailor
taken
tape
tease
temperature
tend
term
thaw
themselves
though
thoughtful
thoughtless
thousand
throne
thrown
tip
tomorrow
ton
toss
touch
touchdown
towel

trade
trap
trapper
trash
trick
trim
trouble
truth
truthful
tuck
twine

U
ugly
unable
unarmed
under
underline
undress
unfair
unfold
unfriendly
United States
universe
unmade
unmated
unsafe
untie
up-and-down
uphill
upon
useless
utter

V
vice
vowel

W
war
warm
warm-blooded
warn
warning
wash
Washington
wasteful
watery
wavy
wax
weak
weigh
well-known
whatever
whatsoever
whenever
wherever
whirl
whom
whose
winter
within

wool
world
worm
worth
worthless
worthy
wouldn't
wound
wristwatch
written

X

Y
yawn
ye
yolk
young

Z
zipper

Word Index: Books 1 and 2

a
able
about
above
according
ace
across
act
add
after
afternoon
again
against
age
ago
aid
ail
air
alive
all
allow
all right
almost
alone
along
alphabet
also
always
am
amuse
amusement
an
and
Andy
anger
angry
animal
Ann(e)
another
answer
ant
any
anybody
anything
anyway
anywhere
are
aren't
arm
armchair
army
around
art
as
ash

ashtray
ask
asleep
at
ate
aunt
awake
away
awoke
awful
baby
babysit
babysitter
back
background
bad
badge
badly
bag
bail
bake
baker
bald
ball
band
bang
bank
banker
bar
barbed
bare
barely
bark
barn
Bart
base
baseball
basin
basket
bat
batch
bath
bathe
bathroom
bathtub
batter
battle
B.C.
be
beach
bean
bear
beat
became
because
become

bed
bedroom
bee
beef
been
beep
beer
beet
before
beg
began
begin
begun
behind
bell
belong
below
belt
Ben
bend
bent
beside
best
bet
better
between
bib
Bible
bid
big
bigwig
bike
bill
billion
Billy
bind
bird
birth
birthday
bit
bite
bitter
black
blackbird
blame
bleach
bleed
bless
blew
blind
blink
blob
block
blood
bloodstream
blouse

blow
blown
blue
bluff
blush
board
boarder
boat
Bob
body
bodyguard
boil
bold
bolt
bomb
bond
bone
bony
book
boot
bore
born
boss
Boston
both
bought
bounce
bouncy
bow
box
boxer
boy
brake
brain
brand
brand-new
brave
bravely
bread
break
breakfast
breath
breathe
breathless
brew
brick
bride
bridge
bright
bring
brink
broke
broom
brother
brotherly
brown

buck
Bucky
bud
buddy
bug
build
bulb
bull
bum
bump
bumper
bumpy
bun
bunch
bunk
bunt
burn
burner
burp
burst
bus
bush
busily
business
bust
busy
busybody
but
butter
buy
by
cab
cage
cake
California
call
calm
calmly
came
camp
camper
can
candy
cane
can't
cap
cape
Cape Cod
car
card
care
careful
careless
carry
cart

carve
case
cash
cast
cat
catbird
catcall
catch
catcher
catfish
catty
caught
cause
cave
ceiling
celebrate
cell
cellar
cent
center
certain
chain
chair
chance
change
Charles
charm
chart
chase
cheap
cheaply
check
checkbook
checkers
cheek
cheese
cheesecake
chess
chessboard
chest
chestnut
chew
chick
chicken
child
children
chill
chin
chocolate
choice
choke
choose
chop
Christ
Christian

Christmas
chrome
church
cigar
cigarette
city
claim
clap
Clark
class
claw
clay
clean
cleaner
clear
click
climb
clip
clock
close
cloth
clothes
cloud
cloudless
cloudy
clown
club
clue
clutch
coach
coal
coast
coaster
coat
cod
code
coffee
coil
coin
Coke
cold
cold-blooded
comb
come
common
commonly
complex
compound
computer
cone
convict
cook
cookbook
cool
cop
cope

copper
copy
copycat
corn
corner
corny
cot
couch
could
couldn't
count
country
countrymen
course
court
cousin
cover
cow
cowboy
crack
cracker
crane
crash
crawl
crazy
creak
cream
creep
creepy
crib
crime
crook
crooked
crop
cross
crouch
crowd
crown
crumb
crunch
crush
crust
cry
cub
cube
cup
cupcake
cupful
curb
cure
curl
curse
curve
cut
cute
cutters

dab	donkey	eight	fetch	forgot	glass	handful	himself
dad	don't	eighteen	few	fork	gleam	handwriting	hind
daddy	door	eighty	fib	form	glitter	handy	hint
dam	doorway	either	fiddle	forty	glue	hang	hip
damp	dope	El Dorado	fiddler	forty-niner	go	hanger	hire
Dan	dot	eleven	field	forward	goal	hangover	his
dance	double	elm	fifteen	fought	God	happen	hit
dancer	down	else	fifty	found	goes	happily	hitter
danger	downhill	employer	fig	four	gold	happy	hive
dare	downstairs	empty	fight	fourteen	golden	hard	hobby
dark	downtown	end	fighter	fourth	gold-plated	hardly	hock
dart	doze	ending	file	Fourth of July	gone	harm	hold
dash	Dr.	England	fill	fox	gong	harmful	holdup
date	drag	English	film	frame	good	harmless	hole
Dave	drain	enough	fin	France	goodness	has	home
dawn	drank	even	find	free	goods	hat	homeless
day	draw	evening	fine	freedom	goose	hatch	home run
dead	dream	ever	fire	freeze	got	hate	homework
deadly	dress	every	firecracker	freezer	gotten	have	honey
deal	dresser	everybody	firm	French	gown	haven't	honeybee
dear	drew	everyone	firmly	fresh	grade	hay	honk
death	drink	everything	first	Friday	grand	he	hood
decide	drive	everywhere	fish	friend	grape	head	hook
deck	driver	example	fist	friendly	grass	heading	hop
deed	drone	expert	fit	from	grave	hear	hope
deep	drop	explain	five	front	graveyard	heard	hopeful
deer	drove	ex-slave	fix	froze	gray	heart	hopeless
den	drown	eye	flag	fry	great	heat	horn
dent	drum	face	flake	fudge	greed	heater	horse
describe	drunk	fact	flaky	full	green	heavy	hose
deserve	dry	factor	flame	fume	grew	heck	hot
desk	duck	fad	flare	fun	grill	he'd	hour
dice	due	fade	flash	fund	grin	heel	house
Dick	dues	fail	flat	funk	grip	held	household
did	dug	faint	flesh	funny	gripe	helicopter	how
diddle	duke	fair	flew	further	groan	hell	however
didn't	dull	fake	float	fuse	groom	hello	hug
die	dumb	fall	flock	fuss	grouch	help	huge
dig	dump	false	flood	fussy	ground	helper	hum
dim	dune	fame	floor	galley	group	helpful	human
dime	dunk	fan	flop	gallon	grow	helpless	hunch
dine	during	fang	flour	game	grown	hen	hundred
diner	dusk	far	flow	gang	guard	her	hung
dinner	dust	fare	flower	gas	guess	herd	hunt
dip	Dutch	farm	flush	gate	guest	here	hunter
dipper	each	farmer	fly	gave	guide	herself	hurt
dirt	ear	fast	fog	George	guilt	he's	hush
dish	early	fat	foggy	germ	guilty	hey	hut
ditch	earn	father	foil	get	gum	hi	I
dive	earth	February	fold	gift	gun	hid	ice
diver	east	fed	folder	gill	guy	hidden	ice-cream
do	Easter	fee	fond	gin	had	hide	icy
dock	easy	feed	food	ginger	hadn't	hide-and-seek	I'd
doctor	eat	feel	fool	gingerbread	hail	hideout	idea
dodge	Eddie	feeling	foot	girl	hair	high	if
does	edge	feet	football	girlfriend	hairless	high-class	ill
doesn't	eel	fell	for	give	hall	high school	I'll
dog	egg	felt	forefeet	glad	ham	hike	I'm
dollar	egghead	female	forget	gland	hammer	hill	important
done	Egypt	fence	forgetful	glare	hand	him	in

ink, kite, lighter, many, mood, nobody, pail, place

inland, kitty, like, map, moon, nod, pain, plain

instead, knee, limb, march, mop, noise, paint, plan

into, knee-deep, lime, March, more, noisily, painter, plane

iron, kneel, limp, mark, morning, noisy, painting, plant

is, knew, Linda, marry, most, none, pair, plate

isn't, knife, line, Mary, mother, no one, pale, platter

it, knit, link, mask, mouse, noon, pan, play

itch, knock, lint, mass, mouth, nope, pancake, player

its, know, lip, mat, mouthful, north, pant, please

it's, known, lipstick, match, move, nose, pants, plot

I've, lab, liquid, mate, movie, nosy, paper, plug

jab, lace, list, math, mow, not, park, plum

jack, lack, lit, matter, mower, note, part, plus

Jack, lacy, little, may, Mr., notebook, party, pod

jacket, lady, live, May, Mrs., nothing, pass, point

jail, lake, living, maybe, Ms., now, past, poke

jam, laid, load, Mayflower, much, nowhere, pat, poker

January, lamb, loaf, me, mud, nude, patch, pole

jar, lame, loan, meal, muddy, numb, path, police

jaw, lamp, lobby, mean, mug, number, paw, policeman

jazz, land, lock, meaning, mugger, nurse, pawn, pond

jeans, lane, log, meant, mule, nut, pay, pool

jeep, lap, lone, meat, munch, nutty, paycheck, poor

jerk, large, lonely, meatless, muse, oar, payday, pop

Jesus, lark, long, meet, must, ocean, payment, popcorn

Jill, last, look, meeting, mute, o'clock, pea, Pope

Jim, late, lord, melt, my, odd, peace, pork

Joan, later, lose, men, myself, of, peach, port

job, laugh, loss, mend, nail, off, pear, pot

jobless, law, lost, mess, name, often, peck, pouch

John, lawful, lot, messy, nap, oil, peek, pound

join, lawn, loud, met, near, okay, peel, pour

joint, lay, loudly, mice, nearly, old, peep, pray

joke, lead, Louise, middle, neat, on, peer, preach

joker, leaf, love, middle-aged, neck, once, pen, preacher

Jones, leak, lovely, might, necktie, one, penny, present

jot, lean, lover, Mike, nectar, one-celled, people, president

joy, learn, low, mile, need, one-half, period, pretzel

jug, least, loyal, mild, needless, only, person, price

July, leave, luck, milk, needy, open, pep, pride

jump, led, luckily, million, nerve, opposite, pepper, print

June, left, lucky, mind, nest, or, pest, prize

junk, leg, lug, mine, net, order, pet, problem

just, lend, lump, miner, never, other, phone, proof

Kate, lent, lunch, mint, new, ouch, pick, proud

keel, Lent, lung, minute, New England, ounce, picture, prune

keep, less, Mack, mirror, news, our, pie, pub

keeper, let, mad, miss, New Year's Day, out, pig, puff

kept, let's, made, mistake, New York, outer, piggy, pull

ketchup, letter, maid, mitt, next, outside, pile, pulse

key, lice, mail, mix, nice, oven, pin, pump

kick, lick, main, mob, nick, over, pine, punch

kid, lid, mainly, mock, nickname, overdone, Ping-Pong, punk

kidnap, lie, make, mom, night, own, pink, punt

kill, life, maker, mommy, nine, pace, Pinocchio, purr

kind, lifeboat, male, Monday, nineteen, pack, pint, purse

king, lifetime, mammal, money, ninety, pad, pipe, push

kiss, lift, man, monkey, nip, page, pit, put

kit, light, manager, month, no, paid, pity, quack

quart	right	saying	shop	slim	spell	stork	table
queen	rim	says	short	sling	spend	storm	tack
queer	ring	scar	shortstop	slip	spent	story	tail
question	rip	scare	shot	slipper	spice	stove	tailor
quick	ripe	scarf	shotgun	slow	spicy	straight	take
quickly	rise	school	should	slowly	spill	strand	taken
quit	risk	score	shouldn't	slum	spit	strange	tale
quite	river	scout	shout	slung	spite	stranger	talk
quote	road	scrap	show	slush	spiteful	straw	tall
race	roar	scrape	shower	sly	splash	stream	tame
rack	roast	scratch	shrank	small	spleen	streamline	tan
rage	rob	scream	shrill	smart	splint	street	tank
raid	robber	screech	shrimp	smash	splinter	stretch	tap
rail	robbery	screen	shrink	smell	split	strike	tape
rain	robe	scribe	shrug	smile	spoil	string	tar
rainbow	rock	scroll	shrunk	smoke	spoon	strip	task
raise	rocky	scrub	shut	smoker	sponge	stripe	taste
rake	rod	sea	shy	snack	sport	stroke	tax
ram	rode	seal	sick	snag	spot	strong	tea
ramp	role	seat	side	snail	sprain	strongly	teach
ran	roll	seaweed	sideways	snake	sprawl	struck	teacher
rang	Rome	second	sight	snap	spray	stuck	team
range	room	see	sign	snappy	spread	study	tear
rank	rope	seed	silent	sneeze	spring	stuff	tease
rare	rose	seek	silly	snip	sprint	sub	teeth
rat	rosy	seem	simple	snob	square	success	television
rate	rot	seen	sin	snore	squeak	successful	tell
raw	round	seep	since	snow	squeal	such	temper
reach	row	self	sinful	so	squeeze	suck	temperature
react	Roy	sell	sing	soak	squirrel	suds	ten
read	royal	send	singer	soap	squirt	Sue	tend
reading	rub	sense	sink	sob	stage	sum	tent
ready	rubber	sent	sip	sock	stagecoach	summer	term
real	rude	sentence	sister	soft	stain	sun	test
really	rug	serve	sit	soil	stair	sunburn	than
reason	rule	set	sitter	sold	stale	Sunday	thank
record	ruler	seven	six	sole	stamp	sung	thankful
red	run	seventeen	six-shooter	solid	stand	sunk	that
reel	rung	seventh	sixteen	some	star	sunlight	that's
refund	runt	seventy	sixty	somebody	stare	sunny	thaw
refuse	rush	shack	size	someone	starfish	sunshine	the
relate	rust	shake	skate	something	start	sure	their
relax	sack	shame	skill	sometimes	starve	surely	them
remain	sad	shape	skin	song	state	surprise	themselves
remember	sadly	share	skirt	soon	stay	Sutter	then
remind	safe	sharp	skunk	sore	steak	swear	there
remove	safely	sharply	sky	sorry	steam	sweat	there's
renew	said	shatter	slacks	sort	steel	sweater	these
rent	sail	shave	slam	sound	steep	sweet	they
repaid	sale	she	slang	soundly	step	swell	thick
report	salt	sheep	slant	soup	stew	swift	thin
rest	same	sheet	slap	sour	stick	swiftly	thing
return	sand	shell	slave	south	sticker	swim	think
rhyme	sang	shift	sleep	space	sticky	swimmer	thinker
rib	sank	shine	sleepily	Spain	still	swipe	third
rice	sat	shiny	sleepless	spank	sting	switch	thirteen
rich	Saturday	ship	sleepy	spare	stink	swizzle	thirty
rid	save	shirt	sleeve	speak	stood	sworn	this
ride	saw	shock	sleeveless	speaker	stop	swung	those
rig	say	shoot	slice	speed	store	tab	though